the

PALEO

diet

the
PALEO
diet

FOOD YOUR BODY IS DESIGNED TO EAT

DANIEL GREEN

PHOTOGRAPHY BY CLARE WINFIELD

KYLE BOOKS

For Harry Charlie Green
A love that lasts forever

First published in
Great Britain in 2014 by

Kyle Books
an imprint of Kyle Cathie Limited
67-69 Whitfield Street
London W1T 4HF

general.enquiries@kylebooks.com

www.kylebooks.com

ISBN: 978 0 85783 227 6

A CIP catalogue record for this title is
available from the British Library.

Text © Daniel Green 2014
Photographs © Clare Winfield 2014
Design © Kyle Books 2014

Editor: Vicki Murrell
Design: Nicky Collings
Photography: Clare Winfield
Food styling: Rosie Reynolds
Styling: Wei Tang
Nutritional analysis: Fiona Hunter
Production: Nic Jones and David Hearn

Colour reproduction by ALTA London

Important notes
All recipe analysis is per portion.

The information and advice contained in
this book is intended as a general guide
to dieting and healthy eating and is not
specific to individuals or their particular
circumstances. This book is not intended to
replace treatment by a qualified practitioner.
Neither the author nor the publishers can be
held responsible for claims arising from the
inappropriate use of any dietary regime. Do
not attempt self-diagnosis or self-treatment
for serious or long-term conditions without
consulting a medical professional or qualified
practitioner.

CONTENTS

WHY I LOVE PALEO

My main priority has always been great-tasting food that is simple and healthy. When I create recipes, I want them to be ones that you will love and share with family and friends and that, as an added bonus, will help you lose weight and feel happy and healthier.

I know a lot about diets. As an overweight young adult, I lost 29kg (4½ stone) and, in the 20 years since then, I have never put the weight back on. I have managed this by cutting out all junk and processed foods and eating fresh fruit, vegetables, fish, meat, seeds and nuts – essentially following the Paleo diet, even before the name and concept were well known. It made sense to me. There is no need to see it as limiting or restrictive, as there is so much you *can* eat. That is what I embraced: delicious, fresh, healthy food that nourishes your body and doesn't sacrifice taste or flavour – and, in fact, doesn't feel like a sacrifice at all.

PEOPLE WHO FOLLOW THE PALEO DIET REPORT A RANGE OF HEALTH BENEFITS:

- Increased energy levels
- Improved sleep
- Clearer skin and healthier looking hair
- Mental clarity
- Improved mood and attitude
- Less bloating and fewer digestive problems
- Fewer headaches and migraines
- Less joint and muscle pain
- Fewer colds and infections

WHAT IS THE PALEO DIET?

Put simply, the Paleo diet is based on the foods your body was designed to eat:

MEAT FISH NUTS SEEDS FRUIT VEGETABLES

The way we eat now is wrong. We have become dependent on synthetic and heavily processed foods that are leading to serious health problems (diabetes and obesity) and, even when we think we're being healthy, we're often eating food groups, such as grains, dairy and legumes, which cause digestive distress and result in chronic symptoms like sluggish energy levels, joint swelling, acid reflux, acne... the list just goes on and on.

There is a better way to eat and to live, and that is through the Paleo plan. Also referred to as the Caveman or Stone Age diet, 'Paleo' refers to the Paleolithic Age, about 2.5 million years ago, when our hunter-gatherer ancestors ate a diet based on meat, fish, nuts, seeds, fruits and vegetables – and thrived.

As our species has evolved, our lifestyle and the foods that we eat have changed dramatically. The Agrarian Revolution introduced grains, dairy, legumes, salt, sugar and alcohol into our diet and, over the last century, with the use of agrochemicals in farming, the upward trend in processed convenience foods, and the use of chemicals as food additives, many believe that our diet has been subjected to more change than at any time over the previous three millennium.

Much of the food that we eat these days has been stripped of its nutrients and pumped full of bad fats, hidden salt, sugar and a plethora of E numbers, such as colours, preservatives, humectants, emulsifiers, artificial flavours, acidity regulators and bulking agents. In fact, it's estimated that adults in the UK eat an average of

2.25kg of additives in just one year and research study after research study points to our declining health. Since 1996, the number of people in the UK with both types of diabetes has increased from 1.4 million to 2.9 million, and by 2025 it is estimated that this number will have risen to 5 million. Cardiovascular disease (CVD) causes over 4 million deaths each year in Europe, and a shocking 41% of men and 33% of women in the UK are overweight.

More and more people are developing hypersensitivities to gluten and lactose and, as this frequently remains undiagnosed, many people live with low-level, chronic symptoms of ill health for years.

It is therefore not surprising that a growing body of evidence is pointing to our modern eating habits as the root cause of many of the chronic diseases common today in the Western world. Our diet bears almost no relation to that of our Paleolithic ancestors and yet our human genetic make-up has changed relatively little since those times.

Many experts believe that the human body has not evolved genetically to deal with this modern way of eating and that the natural diet of our Paleolithic ancestors could be the key to reducing our risk of many diseases and chronic ill health. However, better longterm health is only part of the story, as following the principles of the Paleo diet can bring enhanced energy levels, a healthier immune system and a genuine feeling of wellbeing and vitality.

10 REASONS
TO EAT THE PALEO WAY

1
It's based on unprocessed, whole foods – which means fewer additives, unhealthy trans fats and no hidden sugars or salt.

2
It's low in salt and rich in potassium – which means lower blood pressure.

3
It's high in fruit and vegetables – which means getting your 5 a day is a doddle.

4
It's low in saturated fat and high in healthy fats – which means lower cholesterol and less inflammation.

5
It's rich in protein and fibre – which means it helps you feel fuller for longer and keeps hunger pangs at bay.

6
It helps to recalibrate your metabolism – which will help to shed any unwanted weight.

7
It's gluten-free – which helps to banish bloating and digestive problems.

8
It's low GI – which helps to avoid unhealthy spikes in blood sugar.

9
It's rich in plant-based phytochemicals – which can help reduce the risk of certain types of cancer and conditions like dementia.

10
It helps balance the pH in your body – modern diets encourage the production of acid within the body, which is believed to increase calcium loss from the bone and lead to many other health problems, including kidney stones, arthritis, fatigue, headaches, PMS and skin disorders. In contrast, the Paleo diet helps create a more alkaline environment.

THE PALEO PRINCIPLES

Gastroenterologist Walter L. Voegtlin was one of the first scientists to suggest, in 1975, that following a Paleolithic-style diet could be the key to better health. Since then, there has been a growing body of evidence to support this idea and one of the leading authorities on the diet, Professor Loren Cordain, a Professor at Colorado State University, has published several studies showing the benefits associated with the diet in renowned scientific journals including *The American Journal of Clinical Nutrition* and *The British Journal of Nutrition*.

The core principles of Paleo are that the diet of our Paleolithic ancestors provides the blueprint for what and how we should eat today: eschewing grains, dairy, legumes and vegetable oils and eating high-quality meat, fish, eggs, fruit, vegetables, nuts and seeds that provide us with all the nutrition that we need to lead an active, healthy life.

As you read on, you will see that foods are divided into those to 'avoid', those to eat 'in moderation' and those you are free to eat and enjoy as often as you like. The diet is still evolving and there are a few grey areas regarding what our ancestors did in fact eat in Paleolithic times and so the important thing to remember is that Paleo is not an all-or-nothing plan. The best approach is for you to become attuned to your body and find out what makes you feel happy, healthy and energised. Be mindful of the main Paleo principles, but use them as a basis to create what is right for you.

The Paleo diet is a way of life. It isn't a plan that you follow for a period of time until you achieve a weight-loss goal and then return to your old ways. However, once you've experienced the increased energy levels and feeling of wellbeing that it offers, I guarantee you won't be tempted back by old bad habits. If you're still not convinced, why not give it a try for 2 weeks and see how you feel.

IN MODERATION

SALT

WHY? A high-salt diet will increase the risk of high blood pressure and upset the acid/alkali balance within the body, so use it only in moderation. I have specifically designed the recipes in this book without salt and have used other flavours, such as herbs and spices, so that you won't miss it. It is very easy to acquire a 'taste for salt', but it's also simple to lose this by gradually reducing the amount you add to food and waiting for your taste buds to adapt.

RAW HONEY

WHY? The body processes all forms of sugar in the same way (even honey produces an insulin response in the body), so I recommend you only use raw honey or stevia (in moderation) as sweeteners. Raw honey is honey in its purest, most unprocessed form (it has not been heated or strained and still contains many of the nutrients that the bees put into it). Stevia is a natural, plant-sourced, calorie-free sugar substitute. (For best results, cut out all refined and added sugar for the first 30 days on the diet – you'll find that your taste buds adapt and you enjoy the natural flavour of food without the need to add too much sweetness.)

ALCOHOL

WHY? The occasional glass of wine isn't a problem and yet it is important to remember that alcohol is a toxin so 'in moderation' is key. You should also avoid alcohol that is made from foods on the 'avoid' list, such as beer (made from grain) vodka (made from potatoes), whisky (made from grain) and sake (made from rice).

ROOT VEGETABLES

WHY? The issue of starchy vegetables is one of Paleo's grey areas. Potatoes are definitely on the 'avoid' list, but other root vegetables, like sweet potatoes, don't contain the same antinutrients and don't have such an adverse effect on blood sugar levels. Many hunter-gatherer groups, such as the Kitavans of Papua New Guinea, regularly eat yams, sweet potatoes, taro, and cassava (tapioca), and don't suffer any adverse effects. For this reason I include them here in the 'in moderation' group.

VINEGAR

WHY? Strictly speaking, vinegar wasn't introduced to the human diet until after the Agricultural Revolution, so it wasn't around in the Paleolithic times – if you do want to use vinegar in moderation, choose apple cider vinegar, balsamic or red/white wine vinegar rather than barley malt vinegar. Vinegar can upset the acid/alkali balance within the body, so use it only in moderation.

AVOID

PROCESSED FOODS

E.g. ready meals, fast food

WHY? You don't need a degree in nutrition to know that these foods are bad news, even for those not following a Paleo plan – pumped full of E numbers, salt and sugar, the problem is not just with what has been added but what has been taken away. Processed foods are often stripped of the very nutrients – dietary fibre, vitamins, minerals and phytochemicals – that are good for you.

REFINED AND ADDED SUGARS

E.g. sugar, fructose, high-fructose corn syrup, corn sugar, corn syrup, agave syrup, golden syrup, malt syrup, molasses, rice syrup, jam, marmalade, jelly, ketchup, hoi sin sauce, BBQ sauce, or anything with 'dext' or 'ose' in it

WHY? Unlike natural sugars (i.e. those you find in fruit, which come packaged with other nutrients), refined sugar provides nothing beneficial. All types of sugar (even unrefined natural sugars like honey) encourage the production of insulin which leads to the laying down of fat.

GRAINS AND FOODS CONTAINING GRAINS

E.g. flour, barley, rice, corn, sorghum, amaranth, wild rice, buckwheat, spelt, rye, quinoa, bread, pasta, cookies, biscuits, crackers, cakes, bagels, muffins, pancakes, tortilla, couscous, oats, cereal, beer

WHY? Grains weren't introduced into our diet until after the Agrarian Revolution, so they weren't eaten by our Paleolithic ancestors. Gluten, a protein found in grains, such as wheat, rye and barley, can irritate and damage the lining of the small intestine. This can lead to digestive problems and interfere with the absorption of nutrients from food. Furthermore, in a processed form, grains have a high GI, which means they encourage the release of insulin, which in turn triggers fat storage. They also contain phytic acid, an antinutrient that can block the absorption of important minerals.

DAIRY AND FOODS CONTAINING DAIRY

E.g. milk, butter, cheese, crème fraîche, cream, ice cream, yogurt

WHY? Cow's milk is designed to help calves grow quickly, not for humans to consume throughout their lives, and many believe we lack the digestive enzymes suited to this task. In fact, humans are the only species to continue drinking milk past weaning and adults in most parts of the world do not consume many dairy products. Some estimates suggest that as much as three-quarters of the world is lactose-intolerant, to varying degrees, with symptoms including gas, bloating, cramps, indigestion, nausea, diarrhoea and constipation. Milk and dairy products are also considered to be acid-producing foods, which upset the acid–alkali balance in the body.

BEANS & LEGUMES

E.g. adzuki beans, baked beans, beansprouts, black beans, black-eyed peas, broad beans, cannellini beans, chickpeas, fava beans, kidney beans, lentils, lima beans, mange touts, mung beans, peas, peanuts, peanut butter, pinto beans, sugar snap peas, soy and related products (tofu, miso, soya milk and soy sauce)

WHY? Like cereals, beans and legumes contain antinutrients – lectins and phytic acid – which can irritate and damage the lining of the gut and cause problems such as bloating and diarrhoea. The damage caused by lectins is also thought to create a 'leaky gut', meaning that other large particles can cross the intestinal barrier and enter your blood stream. This is how food sensitivities start.

VEGETABLE AND SEED OILS

E.g. rapeseed/canola oil, palm oil, peanut oil, safflower oil, sunflower oil, soya bean oil, margarine

WHY? These oils are high in omega-6 fatty acids (very different from heart-healthy omega-3s) and promote inflammation – one of the major causes of heart disease and other conditions such as arthritis.

POTATOES

WHY? Potatoes contain saponins – antinutrients that can damage the intestine. Also, because of the type of starch they contain and the way they are prepared, they often have a high GI, which means they cause a spike in blood sugar levels that triggers the release of insulin.

GETTING

STARTED

When you first start on the Paleo diet it can seem a little daunting, but with some careful preparation and planning your new lifestyle will become second nature.

Experts recommend that, for the first 30 days, you stick to the diet rigidly in order to rid yourself of toxins and reset your body's biochemistry. This will also help you to make a clean break with bad habits. If your old way of eating consisted of heavily processed/junk foods or lots of refined carbs or sugar, the first few days on Paleo could be tough. However, even if you believed your old style of eating was healthy and balanced, you might still find Paleo a challenge at the beginning because of the sugar, salt and additives that are 'hidden' in many foods that claim to be natural and healthy. Many people start to feel the benefits of the Paleo diet within the first few days, but for others it can take a little longer. However, if you stick with it,

you will start to feel and see the benefits and, once that happens, there's no looking back.

THE PALEO KITCHEN

A key part of the preparation for the Paleo diet is transforming your kitchen into a Paleo-friendly place. Clear all the forbidden foods from your fridge, freezer, shelves and cupboards, and re-stock with all the foods from the list on pages 16–17.

I also recommend that you prepare your own food as much as you can, as then you will know exactly what is in it. When eating out, always enquire how the dish is made if you have any doubts. Also, when shopping, always read the food label and be on your guard for any ingredients you don't recognise, with names that are hard to pronounce. Instead, look out for these guarantees of health and quality:

WATCH WORDS

· Organic, locally grown, seasonal produce – organic fruit and vegetables, grown without chemicals, are not just better for the environment, they are better for your body, because they are more nutritious.

· Grass-fed, free-range – meat reared this way has a better fatty acid balance (i.e. more omega-3 fats, fewer omega-6 fats). Eat meat that is free from antibiotic and other residues.

· Free-range – chickens grubbing in a field are far healthier than ones kept in cages and studies have shown their eggs are nutritionally superior.

· Sustainably sourced – buy fish and shellfish from responsible sources for environmental reasons, preferably wild-caught rather than farm-raised fish, as the latter are often fed chemicals and antibiotics and have lower levels of protein and omega-3s.

THE 80/20 RULE

If the idea of never having a bagel, a bowl of muesli or a glass of wine ever again fills you with terror, don't worry. The Paleo diet has an 80/20 rule, which means that, providing you stick to the rules 80% of the time, you don't need to be quite so strict for the other 20%. You can lapse a little and treat yourself to the odd slice of toast or sugary dessert. However, I recommend that you start by following the diet to the letter for at least a few weeks, just to see how much better you feel. And, with this book of fantastic recipes, you'll struggle to find a reason to cook anything else!

A 10-DAY PALEO TRIAL

IN ONE STUDY, PUBLISHED IN THE *EUROPEAN JOURNAL OF CLINICAL NUTRITION*, SCIENTISTS FROM THE UNIVERSITY OF CALIFORNIA FOUND THAT, AFTER JUST 10 DAYS OF EATING A PALEO DIET, VOLUNTEERS HAD IMPROVED BLOOD SUGAR CONTROL, INCREASED SENSITIVITY TO INSULIN, REDUCED BLOOD PRESSURE AND REDUCED LEVELS OF TOTAL CHOLESTEROL, LDL OR 'BAD' CHOLESTEROL, AND TRIGLYCERIDES IN THEIR BLOOD.

WHAT TO BUY

MEAT, FISH & EGGS

fresh meat, poultry, game and offal – beef, chicken, duck, game birds, goat, lamb, pork, rabbit, turkey, veal, venison, wild boar

eggs – hen's, quail's or duck's, even emu's

fish (and fish eggs) and shellfish (tinned and fresh)

FRUIT & VEG

apples, apricots, bananas, berries, cherries, citrus fruits, cranberries, dates, dragon fruit, figs, grapes, kiwis, lychees, mangos, melons, nectarines, passion fruit, peaches, pears, persimmons, pineapples, plums, pomegranates, star fruit

artichokes, asparagus, aubergines, butternut squash, Brussels sprouts, broccoli, cabbages, carrots, cauliflowers, celery, courgettes, cucumbers, kale, kohlrabi, leeks, lettuces, marrows, mushrooms, okra, olives, onions, pak choi, parsnips, pumpkins, radishes, spinach, watercress, tomatoes, turnips

sea vegetables – kombu, nori, wakame, other seaweeds and algaes

tinned fruit and vegetables (but make sure they are sugar- and sodium-free)

NUTS

almonds, Brazil nuts, cashews, chestnuts, hazelnuts, macadamias, pecans, pine nuts, pistachios, walnuts (NB peanuts are not Paleo-friendly because they are legumes not nuts)

nut butters – almond, cashew, macadamia

almond flour – blanched almonds, ground up into a fine powder – a great ingredient for baking and can be used in place of regular wheat flour

SEEDS

flaxseed, pumpkin seeds, sesame seeds, sunflower seeds

OILS & FATS

avocado oil, coconut oil, flaxseed oil, hazelnut oil, macadamia nut oil, olive oil, sesame oil, walnut oil

lard, tallow

DRINKS

filtered or spring water, herbal tea, coconut water, freshly juiced fruit and vegetables

FLAVOURINGS & SAUCES	fish sauce – many fish sauces are not Paleo as they have added fructose and sugar or hydrolysed wheat protein. However, the Red Boat brand is a rare exception – it's only made from two ingredients (freshly caught wild black anchovies and sea salt) and is minimally processed.
	curry paste – many curry pastes are Paleo, just make sure you read the label to check the ingredients. It's also very easy to make yourself.
	sea salt – produced through evaporation of ocean water or lake seawater and so undergoes little processing. Table salt is usually mined and contains additives, which is why sea salt is better.
	coconut aminos – a soy-free seasoning sauce made from coconut tree sap, this is a great substitute for soy sauce
	mustard – make sure it is gluten- and dairy-free
	tomato paste and sun-dried tomato paste – make sure it is gluten-free with no added sugar or salts
	meat, fish and vegetable stocks – organic and low-salt are the best options, or it's very simple to make your own
	arrowroot powder – a natural thickener that can be used in place of cornstarch or wheat flour to thicken sauces
	herbs and spices – add great flavour to food and are a source of many vitamins, minerals and phytochemicals
SWEETENERS	raw honey – add in place of sugar when you want sweetness. Raw honey is often solid and you just need to warm it up a little to get it to a liquid state.
	stevia – a plant that has been used as a sweetener for centuries in Paraguay and Brazil (now commonly available as naturally sourced sugar substitute)
COCONUT	coconut flour – natural, dried coconut that is ground into a fine powder. Also a great substitute for wheat flour.
	coconut milk – a great substitute for milk and makes the most delicious curries. Look for brands that don't contain guar gum or preservatives and always go for the 'light' version to keep the fat content low.
	shredded, unsweetened coconut

FAQ

IS THE DIET SUITABLE FOR CHILDREN?

The Paleo diet is a nutrient-dense diet and can provide all the nutrition that a growing child needs. In fact, some people would argue that, because it cuts out heavily processed/refined foods and things like sweets and biscuits, the Paleo diet is better for children than a traditional Western diet. Having said that, however, it's important to remember that children are still developing and growing and as a result they have needs, particularly for nutrients like calcium, which should be taken very seriously. In practical terms, it is important to plan their diet carefully to ensure that it provides enough energy (calories) and other nutrients to support their growth. While low-carb diets are fine and dandy for fully grown adults, carbs are a useful source of energy for a growing child, so many parents relax the rules slightly and add in a few unprocessed carbs like potatoes, sweet potatoes and other starchy vegetables.

IS THE DIET SUITABLE FOR PEOPLE WITH DIABETES?

One of the benefits of the Paleo plan is improved insulin sensitivity and better blood sugar control – two big plus points for people with type 2 diabetes. Furthermore, diabetics have a greater risk of heart disease, so the fact that the diet is low in salt and rich in healthy fats is another bonus. However, while there is no restriction on the amount of fruit eaten on the diet, it does contain natural sugars, so diabetics need to watch the amount they consume carefully. People with insulin-dependent (type 1) diabetes should discuss the diet with their dietician or doctor before giving it a try.

IS THE PALEO DIET SUITABLE FOR VEGETARIANS?

Meat and fish were an integral part of the diet of Paleolithic Man, and they are a major source of protein in the Paleo diet. Grains and legumes, an important source of protein in many vegetarian diets, are not allowed on the Paleo diet and so the truth is that it can be difficult to follow as a vegetarian. I recommend vegetarians consult a dietician to discuss adapting the diet to their needs before giving it a try.

I'M PREGNANT. CAN I FOLLOW THE PALEO PLAN?

Yes, the Paleo diet is perfectly capable of providing all the nutrients a pregnant woman needs and can even help reduce the risk of some pregnancy-related conditions, such as gestational diabetes.

WILL THE DIET HELP ME LOSE WEIGHT?

Although Paleo is not designed as a weight-loss diet, many people find that it helps them shed unwanted weight. There are several explanations for this: cutting out highly refined/high GI carbs reduces the amount of insulin that the body needs to produce and, as insulin encourages the body to lay down fat, the reduction in insulin makes it easier to lose weight. Another theory is that it helps to recalibrate your metabolism so that you burn more calories. The fact that the diet is high in protein and fibre will also help, because these nutrients help you feel full quicker and for longer so you're less likely to overeat.

HOW CAN I MAKE SURE I GET ENOUGH CALCIUM ON THE DIET?

Dairy products are rich in calcium, which is important for strong, healthy bones. However, there are plenty of other non-dairy, Paleo-friendly sources:

· fish that is eaten with bones, such as sardines or tinned salmon

· kale and other leafy green veg

· nuts and seeds, particularly almonds and sesame seeds

· dried apricots and figs

· oranges

	RDA calcium		Calcium (mg)
Children 4–6 years	450mg	100g sardines	500mg
Children 7–10 years	550mg	80g steamed kale	120mg
Boys 11–18 years	1000mg	25g almonds	60mg
Girls 11–18 years	800mg	2 tbsp almond butter	86mg
Men and women	700mg	100g tinned salmon	300mg
Breast-feeding women	1250mg	25g dried apricots	25mg
Women after menopause	1000mg	1 tbsp sesame seeds	100mg
		1 orange	70mg
		80g steamed broccoli	32mg
		100g watercress	170mg

HOW TO
USE THIS BOOK

The Paleo recipes in this book are guaranteed to bring you many health benefits, and weight loss is often simply an additional bonus. However, if you have bought this book with a specific weight-loss goal in mind, I have designed it in a way that I believe will maximise your efforts and that I hope you will find beneficial.

As I have said, as a teenager I piled on the pounds. I realised that, in order to lose weight, I needed to change the way that I thought about food and so I set about researching the best, most effective way to go about this. I became very interested in the work of the New York physician, William Howard Hay, who was the first to develop the concept of 'food combining' and whose theories have proved extremely influential in the world of modern dieting.

Hay's research gave him the idea that certain foods require an acid pH environment for digestion, whereas other foods require the opposite, an alkaline environment. As most meals contain a mix of the two, the digestion of both cannot take place at the same time and the result is often a chemical imbalance that leads to many symptoms of digestive distress. Hay's solution to this problem was to create meals from alkali-forming foods (such as fruits and vegetables) and from acid-forming foods (concentrated proteins such as meat, game, fish, cheese and eggs) and never to combine the two. Concentrated carbohydrates or starch foods (grains, bread, all foods containing flour, all sugars and foods containing sucrose, but not the naturally occurring sugars found in fruit) were then grouped into another acid-forming category, but these again were to be kept separate from proteins as they, too, needed different conditions for digestion.

In order to lose weight, I incorporated Hay's approach into my eating habits and have never looked back. As it worked for me I believe it can work for you, too, and so in this book you will find that the recipes are colour coded.

The green recipes are dishes that are based around alkali-forming fruits and vegetables, while the red recipes feature acid-forming proteins. To ensure a balanced diet and the best weight-loss results, I recommend that you choose red recipes for an entire day and then switch to green recipes the next day and alternate throughout the week. However, you could also start with a red breakfast and then have a green lunch and go back to red for dinner – whichever you prefer. And, of course, if you simply want to follow the Paleo plan, just ignore the colour-coding and go with any recipe that takes your fancy. Whatever your preferred approach, I promise you excellent results.

So get cooking! Start following these recipes today, and join the Paleo revolution!

BREAKFASTS
& BRUNCHES

You'll be served these little steamed egg soups for breakfast in most hotels in Asia and they're also popular as an appetiser. Their texture should be smooth and bubble-free and the key is to simmer them on as low a heat as possible, for as long as possible.

JAPANESE SAVOURY CUSTARD (CHAWANMUSHI)

153 calories | 10.3g fat | 2.7g saturates | 0.3g sugar | 0.9g salt | 15.5g protein | 0.2g fibre

Serves 4

6 eggs
vegetable stock or dashi
– volume to equal that
of the eggs
1 teaspoon Paleo-
friendly fish sauce,
such as Red Boat (not
necessary if using
dashi)
8 large cooked prawns
4 straw or shiitake
mushrooms, very
thinly sliced
1 spring onion, cut into
matchsticks

Crack the eggs into a medium-sized bowl and, using chopsticks, lightly whisk until blended, without incorporating too much air. Stir in the dashi or stock and add the fish sauce, if using.

Divide the mixture between 4 small serving bowls, each about the size of a ramekin.

Cover these bowls or wrap them in clingfilm and steam over a low heat (the water should be at a gentle simmer) for 15–20 minutes, or until the eggs are set – a bamboo steamer is great for this.

Immediately transfer the bowls to the refrigerator to chill for at least 3 hours or overnight.

Unwrap the custards. Top with the prawns, mushrooms and spring onions and serve.

 TIP DASHI IS A TRADITIONAL JAPANESE BROTH MADE FROM BONITO FLAKES AND KOMBU (KELP – HIGH IN POTASSIUM, CALCIUM AND IODINE AS WELL AS VITAMINS A AND C). IT OFTEN HAS RICE WINE OR VINEGAR AND SOY SAUCE ADDED FOR FLAVOUR, BUT YOU CAN REPLACE THESE WITH WITH PALEO-FRIENDLY COCONUT WATER VINEGAR (SOMETIMES JUST CALLED COCONUT VINEGAR) AND COCONUT AMINOS (MADE FROM RAW COCONUT TREE SAP AND SUN-DRIED SEA SALT – IT TASTES JUST LIKE SOY SAUCE).

Pancakes always make a delicious weekend brunch – and who says you can't have them on a Paleo diet? Simply replace regular flour with coconut and almond flour and you can achieve light, fluffy, gluten-free results.

PANCAKES WITH
BERRIES AND MAPLE SYRUP

532 calories | 37.6g fat | 5.7g saturates | 18.5g sugar | 0.4g salt | 24.5g protein | 12g fibre

Serves 2

100g almond flour
1 tablespoon coconut
 flour
3 eggs
50ml water
75ml prune juice
¼ teaspoon freshly
 grated nutmeg
olive oil spray
200g fresh berries
1 tablespoon grade B
 maple syrup or melted
 raw honey

In a large mixing bowl, whisk the flours, eggs and water together until you have a smooth batter. Any lumps should soon disappear with a little mixing. Whisk in the prune juice and nutmeg and set aside for a minute or two.

Place a non-stick frying pan over a medium heat and allow to get hot – about 2–3 minutes. Spray the pan with a little oil and add a spoonful of batter (it is best not to crowd the pan, so make these pancakes one at a time). Let the batter bubble a little and cook for a minute, then flip and cook for 1–2 minutes on the reverse side.

Turn onto a plate and serve with fresh berries and a drizzle of maple syrup or honey.

TIP WHEN YOU MAKE THESE PANCAKES, TRY AND COOK THEM AS SOON AS THE BATTER IS MADE, AS THE COCONUT FLOUR CAN SWELL AND THICKEN OVER TIME – IT DOESN'T KEEP OVERNIGHT.

TIP THE PALEO PLAN CUTS OUT ALL PROCESSED, REFINED SUGARS BUT DOES ALLOW A FEW NATURAL SWEETENERS. THE BEST TYPES TO USE ARE GRADE B MAPLE SYRUP, WHICH IS 100% PURE AND DISTILLED NATURALLY, AND RAW HONEY, WHICH IS AGAIN UNPROCESSED AND CONTAINS ALL THE NUTRIENTS THE BEES PUT INTO IT.

Everyone loves sushi, but rice is not allowed on the Paleo plan, so these rolls are the next best thing. I first made them for a boutique hotel in Bangkok called VIE and they are still on the menu, though I change up the fillings every now and again.

NO-RICE
BREAKFAST SUSHI

406 calories | 27.5g fat | 5.9g saturates | 0g sugar | 4.5g salt | 41g protein | 0.6g fibre

Serves 2

4 eggs
freshly ground black
  pepper
½ tablespoon olive oil
2 large sheets of seaweed
  paper (nori)
2 tablespoons chopped
  chives
225g smoked salmon

Crack 2 of the eggs into a bowl and beat with a fork until smooth. Season with freshly ground black pepper.

Heat a heavy non-stick frying pan over a high heat and add the oil. When hot, tip the eggs into the pan. Swirl to coat the base thoroughly and allow the eggs to set slightly. Cook for 1–2 minutes. Remove from the heat, tip the omelette onto a plate (do not fold) and repeat the process with the 2 remaining eggs.

Lay a sheet of the seaweed paper out flat on a clean kitchen surface and place one of the omelettes on top. Scatter with chives and layer half the smoked salmon on top. Season to taste.

Fold the bottom edge of the seaweed over the filling, then roll it up firmly. Dampen the top border with a little water to help it seal. Repeat with the second omelette and sheet of seaweed paper.

Using a serrated knife, cut off the ends to neaten them and slice each roll into 4–6 rounds. Serve immediately.

 VARIATION BACON IS ALSO A VERY TASTY ADDITION TO A BREAKFAST SUSHI ROLL. HOWEVER, ENSURE THAT YOU BUY THE BEST-QUALITY MEAT YOU CAN FIND – IT WON'T BE AS HEAVILY PROCESSED AS THE MASS-PRODUCED, CHEAPER VARIETIES.

Soufflés often get people a little scared. However, they're as easy as anything so please don't be intimidated. They do deflate a little when you take them out of the oven, but don't panic if this happens – it doesn't mean it's a disaster!

EGG SOUFFLÉ
OMELETTE

314 calories | 19.5g fat | 5g saturates | 2g sugar | 2.4g salt | 34.1g protein | 0.8g fibre

Serves 1

2 eggs, plus 2 egg whites
1 teaspoon olive oil
6 cherry tomatoes, halved
3 slices of ham (very good quality, not pre-sliced), chopped
freshly ground black pepper
1 tablespoon chopped chives

Preheat the grill to high.

Crack the eggs, separating the yolks from the whites in separate bowls. Add the 2 extra egg whites.

Whisk the whites vigorously for about a minute until light and fluffy, then whisk the yolks and add them to the whites. Fold in carefully.

Heat the oil in a wide, non-stick frying pan with a heatproof handle and add the egg mix, swirling the pan so it coats the bottom. Leave to cook for a couple of minutes, then add the tomatoes and ham and season with black pepper.

Transfer the pan to the grill and leave for a few minutes until the eggs are puffed up, soufflé-like and golden.

Remove from the heat and slide onto a plate. Scatter the chives on top and serve immediately.

 TIP EGGS MAKE THE PERFECT BREAKFAST IF YOU'RE TRYING TO LOSE WEIGHT AS THE PROTEIN AND FAT HELP SUSTAIN YOUR ENERGY LEVELS, ARMING YOU AGAINST THOSE CRAVINGS FOR A MID-MORNING SNACK.

Sun-dried tomatoes are a great ingredient to have stocked in your Paleo-friendly kitchen as they have a rich flavour and an almost meaty texture, so guarantee a very satisfying start to the day – especially nice for a weekend brunch.

OMELETTE WITH
SUN-DRIED TOMATOES

350 calories | 27g fat | 6.3g saturates | 3.8g sugar | 0.9g salt | 24.4g protein | 1.7g fibre

Serves 4

12 eggs
freshly ground black
  pepper
1 tablespoon olive oil
1½ red onions, thinly
  sliced
2 tablespoons chopped
  sun-dried tomatoes
12 cherry tomatoes,
  halved
a handful of basil leaves,
  shredded, plus extra
  to serve
75g watercress

It's best to cook one omelette at a time, so start by breaking 3 eggs into a large mixing bowl and beating them lightly with a fork. Season with a little black pepper.

Turn the grill on to its highest setting.

Heat a drizzle of olive oil in a large, non-stick frying pan and fry the onion until soft and slightly caramelised. Transfer the onion to a plate and set aside.

Add the beaten egg to the frying pan, swirling the pan to cover the base as it sets.

Scatter a quarter of the cooked onion, sun-dried tomato, cherry tomatoes and basil over the top of the omelette and slide the pan under the hot grill for 1–2 minutes or until golden.

Slide the omelette onto a plate and keep warm while you cook the remaining omelettes. Serve with some fresh, peppery watercress and a little extra basil.

If you feel hungry and need a larger portion, add more egg whites to the pan. Egg whites have all the protein, which helps you stay fuller for longer, without the fat of the yolk.

SCRAMBLED EGGS
WITH AVOCADO SALSA

450 calories | 38.2g fat | 9.4g saturates | 3.5g sugar | 0.7g salt | 24.5g protein | 4.6g fibre

Serves 2

1 ripe Hass avocado,
    chopped
a handful of basil
    leaves, torn
1 large tomato, deseeded
    and chopped
2 spring onions, finely
    chopped
6 eggs
freshly ground black
    pepper
½ tablespoon olive oil

Place the avocado, basil, tomato and spring onion in a bowl and mix to combine.

In a separate bowl, lightly whisk the eggs and season with a few grinds of black pepper.

Heat the olive oil in a non-stick saucepan over a medium heat. Add the eggs to the pan and let the mixture rest for about half a minute, then stir with a wooden spoon, lifting and folding and turning until they are lightly sct and slightly runny in places.

Remove from the heat and leave the eggs for a few seconds to continue cooking.

Divide the eggs between 2 plates and spoon the avocado salsa alongside.

 TIP YOU CAN REDUCE THE AMOUNT OF AVOCADO AND UP THE QUANTITY OF TOMATO TO LOWER THE FAT CONTENT, BUT DON'T FORGET THAT AVOCADO IS A SOURCE OF HEALTHY, MONOUNSATURATED FAT THAT IS QUICKLY BURNED FOR ENERGY.

This healthy breakfast is perfect all-round. The salmon is an excellent source of omega-3 fatty acids – essential for brain function, warding off heart disease and maintaining healthy hair and nails – while poaching eggs is the best way to cook them without adding any extra fat into the equation.

POACHED EGGS
WITH SMOKED SALMON

310 calories | 19.8g fat | 5.1g saturates | 0.4g sugar | 3.9g salt | 33.1g protein | 0g fibre

Serves 4

150ml white vinegar
450g smoked salmon
4 eggs
2 tablespoons chopped
   chives
freshly ground black
   pepper

Fill a saucepan just over half full with cold water and bring it to the boil. Add the vinegar (the ratio should be about 4:1, water to vinegar).

Meanwhile, divide the smoked salmon between 4 serving plates. When the water is at a fast boil, crack one egg into one side of the pan and another egg into the other side. (I recommend doing no more than 2 at a time, or the pan boils over.) Cook the eggs for 3–4 minutes.

Remove the eggs with a slotted spoon and place in a bowl of tepid water to keep warm while you cook the other eggs.

When all the eggs are poached, you can refresh the water in the bowl to completely remove the taste of vinegar.

When ready to serve, place an egg on each plate of salmon, scatter with fresh chives and season with a few grinds of black pepper.

TIP IT IS GOOD TO ADD VINEGAR TO THE WATER WHEN POACHING EGGS AS IT HELPS THE WHITES TO FIRM UP FASTER. FRESH EGGS ARE EASIER TO POACH AS THEY HOLD THEIR SHAPE BETTER – THE WHITES GATHER AROUND THE YOLKS, RESULTING IN A ROUNDER, PERFECT, POACHED EGG SHAPE.

These cookies are a real treat, as very few baking ingredients are compatible with the Paleo diet. However, this recipe creates delicious, crumbly coconut biscuits without using any butter – genius!

CRUMBLY
COCONUT COOKIES

125 calories | 6.3g fat | 3.8g saturates | 3.7g sugar | 0.2g salt | 6.1g protein | 5.6g fibre

Makes 10-12 cookies

100ml light coconut milk
4 eggs, beaten
130g coconut flour
1½ tablespoons raw
   honey

Preheat the oven to 200°C/gas mark 6 and line a baking sheet with greaseproof paper.

Put all the ingredients in a large bowl and stir to mix well. As it becomes like a soft dough, use your hands to combine.

Spoon the mixture into 10–12 small rounds, about 2.5cm in diameter, and place them, spaced evenly apart, on the baking tray. Bake in the oven for 10–12 minutes, or until golden brown.

Remove from the oven and allow to cool for a few minutes, then turn out onto a wire rack to cool completely before serving.

 TIP THESE COOKIES CAN CRUMBLE IF YOU OVERCOOK THEM, SO ERR ON THE SIDE OF CAUTION AND SLIGHTLY UNDERCOOK, LEAVING THEM TO COOK THROUGH WHILE THEY COOL.

This fruit cup sundae provides you with a great boost of breakfast energy. If you want to lower the carbohydrates, just swap the bananas for more berries and citrus fruits. You can make this the night before to have on the run.

FRUIT CUP
SUNDAE

498 calories | 28.6g fat | 3.6g saturates | 47.7g sugar | 0g salt | 9g protein | 6.3g fibre

Serves 4

4 ripe bananas, peeled
300g mixed berries
   (strawberries and
   raspberries are great)
60g unsalted walnuts
60g unsalted cashew
   nuts
60g unsalted pecans
3 tablespoons raw honey,
   melted

In a bowl, mash the bananas with a fork and set aside. If using strawberries, cut them into 1cm slices and set aside.

Place the nuts in a sealed plastic bag and bash with a rolling pin a few times to crush. Transfer to a bowl, add the honey and stir to mix well.

In individual glass bowls or cocktail glasses, layer the banana, berries and nuts, repeating until you reach the top.

 TIP RAW HONEY HAS ANTISEPTIC, ANTIBIOTIC, ANTIFUNGAL AND ANTIBACTERIAL PROPERTIES AND IT NEVER SPOILS! IT IS GENERALLY MORE SOLID THAN REGULAR HONEY, BUT IF YOU HEAT IT A LITTLE IT WILL MELT AND CAN BE DRIZZLED JUST LIKE LIQUID HONEY.

This is a vitamin-rich power breakfast smoothie – essential for those days when you wake up feeling sluggish. The apples cover the detox angle, while the kale, banana and honey will provide you with energy to spare.

POWER BREAKFAST BLEND

183 calories | 6g fat | 4.9g saturates | 29.5g sugar | 0.1g salt | 2g protein | 4.3g fibre

Serves 2

1 apple, cored
1 banana
a large handful (40g) of spinach or kale
1 tablespoon coconut oil
1 teaspoon vanilla essence
1 teaspoon ground cinnamon
1 teaspoon raw honey

Blend everything in a food processor or blender until smooth and serve over ice.

Raw honey and grade B maple syrup are the natural sweeteners allowed on Paleo. You can use either in any of these recipes. The mint is a must though, as it lifts this smoothie with a burst of fresh flavour – lovely in the morning!

ENERGISER

333 calories | 13.3g fat | 11.4g saturates | 44.2g sugar | trace salt | 4.8g protein | 3.7g fibre

Serves 2

2 ripe bananas, peeled
1 tablespoon raw honey
200g strawberries
150ml coconut milk
a handful of ice
a few mint leaves, to serve

Place all the ingredients except the mint in a blender and whizz until smooth. Serve with a sprig of mint.

 TIP THE PALEO DIET DOES NOT ENCOURAGE CAFFEINE. HOWEVER, IF YOU ARE FOLLOWING THE PLAN LONG TERM, IT IS POSSIBLE YOU MIGHT INDULGE A LITTLE FROM TIME TO TIME. ADDING AN ESPRESSO SHOT TO THIS SMOOTHIE WILL PROVIDE YOU WITH AN EXTRA BOOST OF ENERGY, SO KEEP IT IN RESERVE FOR WHEN YOU NEED IT MOST.

This is such a delicious way to start the day. The mango has natural sugar and carbohydrates to get you going in the morning, while the coconut milk will keep you feeling full until lunch.

MANGO
BREAKFAST SMOOTHIE

252 calories | 14.2g fat | 11.4g saturates | 29g sugar | 0.3g salt | 2.6g protein | 8.2g fibre

Serves 2

2 ripe mangoes, peeled
    and stoned
250ml light coconut milk
½ teaspoon ground
    cinnamon

Place all the mango flesh, plus the coconut milk and cinnamon, into a blender and purée until smooth. Serve over ice.

TIP TRYING TO GET ALL THE FLESH OUT OF A MANGO CAN LEAVE YOU WITH A BIG, JUICY MESS. THE BEST WAY TO DO IT IS TO TAKE A SHARP KNIFE AND SLICE THE FRUIT VERTICALLY, AS CLOSE TO EITHER SIDE OF THE STONE AS POSSIBLE. NEXT, HOLD EACH MANGO SLICE FLESH-SIDE UP AND SCORE THE FLESH IN A GRID PATTERN ALL THE WAY DOWN TO THE SKIN. NOW TURN THE SKIN INSIDE OUT AND CUT THE MANGO CUBES INTO A BOWL, ADDING ALL THE JUICES THAT ARE LEFT ON THE PLATE, AND THERE IS NO WASTE!

LIGHT MEALS, SNACKS & SIDES

This recipe contains all the good fats, plus lots of protein, so it will keep you feeling full and banish hunger cravings between meals. Quail's eggs might seem elegant and decadent, but they are not at all expensive. Look in your local Asian supermarkets to get the best prices.

SALMON, AVOCADO AND QUAIL'S EGGS

504 calories | 41.7g fat | 9.3g saturates | 0.8g sugar | 2.5g salt | 30.2g protein | 3.4g fibre

Serves 4

12 quail's eggs
1 tablespoon white
    vinegar
3 tablespoons olive oil
1 teaspoon Dijon
    mustard
300g smoked salmon
2 avocados, thinly sliced
1 lemon, quartered
dill, to garnish

Place the quail's eggs in a saucepan, cover with water and bring to the boil. Cook for 4–5 minutes, then drain and allow to cool before peeling.

Make the dressing by whisking together the vinegar, olive oil and mustard.

Slice the quail's eggs in half and divide them between 4 plates, along with the salmon and avocado.

Drizzle the vinaigrette on top and serve with lemon wedges and a scattering of fresh dill.

 TIP TINY, SPECKLED QUAIL'S EGGS ARE INCREDIBLY PRETTY AND MAKE A VERY CLASSY ADDITION TO MANY SOUPS, SALADS AND APPETISERS. THEY'RE ALSO LOW IN CALORIES, RICH IN PROTEIN AND FULL OF ESSENTIAL NUTRIENTS, SUCH AS VITAMIN D AND B12, SELENIUM AND CHOLINE.

I have worked a lot throughout Asia – mainly in Hong Kong, Thailand and Malaysia – and I love to cook this style of food, as it's so full of delicious flavour and is easy to make at home. This is a perfect example. Add a little chilli and Hoi Sin sauce if you are not following the Paleo plan so strictly.

PORK AND
BEEF CABBAGE ROLLS

213 calories | 9g fat | 3.6g saturates | 3.6g sugar | 0.1g salt | 26.8g protein | 1.9g fibre

Serves 4

15–20 cabbage leaves
200g lean minced beef
200g lean minced pork
1 onion, finely chopped
3 garlic cloves, crushed
2 bird's eye chillies,
  finely chopped
1 litre vegetable stock

Bring a large pan of water to the boil and blanch the cabbage leaves for 1–2 minutes, then drain, refresh in iced water and set aside.

In a bowl, mix the beef, pork, onion, garlic and chilli, stirring to incorporate well.

Lay a cabbage leaf on a clean surface and place a large spoonful of the mince mixture in the centre. Fold the sides of the leaf over to cover the filling and then roll into a small parcel, pinning with a cocktail stick to seal. Repeat until you have used up all the filling.

In a large saucepan, bring the stock to the boil. Carefully lower the cabbage rolls into the pan and simmer for 15 minutes or until the meat filling is cooked through.

Serve the cabbage rolls in a bowl with a ladleful of the stock.

 TIP DON'T FORGET TO REFRESH THE LEAVES IN ICED WATER AS THIS WILL ENSURE THE CABBAGE STOPS COOKING AND STAYS A VIBRANT GREEN.

Serve this at a party and I guarantee you'll impress your guests – the presentation is fantastic. To achieve a perfectly shaped tower, all you need is a pastry ring, but if you don't have one to hand, it's easy to make your own by taking the top and bottom off a tuna can.

SALMON AND
AVOCADO TOWER

397 calories | 31.7g fat | 5.9g saturates | 1.6g sugar | 0.2g salt | 25.2g protein | 3.8g fibre

Serves 4

2 x 200g skinless salmon
    fillets
juice of 1 lemon
2 tablespoons olive oil
4–6 chives, finely
    chopped, plus extra
    to garnish
2 ripe avocados, peeled,
    halved and stoned
2 spring onions, finely
    chopped
½ red onion, finely
    chopped
freshly ground black
    pepper
80g salmon roe

Using a sharp knife, chop the salmon into very small cubes (making sure you discard any bones you find). Transfer the salmon to a bowl and pour over half the lemon juice.

Add in the olive oil and chives and mix together well, then set aside.

Scoop the avocado flesh into a bowl and mash with a fork. Squeeze over the remaining lemon juice so it does not discolour. Add the spring onion and red onion and mix in well with a few grinds of black pepper.

Place 4 small pastry rings on 4 individual plates and fill each a quarter full with a layer of avocado. Add a layer of cured salmon to almost reach the top of the mould, and then top with a layer of salmon roe. Finish with a garnish of chives and serve.

 TIP YOU CAN ALSO USE TROUT ROE FOR THIS RECIPE, AS IT'S VERY TASTY AND A LITTLE LESS EXPENSIVE THAN SALMON ROE.

I love tuna tartare and have created and tasted many different versions over the years. However, this one, representing the flavours of Asia, has to be my favourite. Add a little green chilli if you like things spicy.

ASIAN TUNA
TARTARE

322 calories | 20.7g fat | 4.2g saturates | 1.8g sugar | 0.2g salt | 31.3g protein | 2.6g fibre

Serves 4

2 x 250g tuna steaks
 (very fresh)
1 tablespoon sesame
 seeds, plus extra
 to garnish
2 tablespoons sesame oil
2 tablespoons lemon juice
½ red onion, finely
 chopped
4 spring onions, chopped
1 avocado, finely cubed
a handful of fresh
 coriander, plus extra
 to garnish

Finely chop the tuna steaks and then place in a large bowl with the sesame seeds, sesame oil, lemon juice, red onion, spring onion and avocado. Mix well. Add the coriander to the bowl and mix together well.

Spoon the mixture onto a plate. Sometime a loose presentation is nice but, if you want to serve it like a traditional tartare, use a chef's ring as a mould and press the tuna mixture down firmly so it holds its shape.

To serve, remove the ring, if using, and scatter over a few sesame seeds and some extra coriander.

 TIP SESAME OIL IS WONDERFULLY RICH IN FLAVOUR. HOWEVER, A LITTLE GOES A LONG WAY, SO ADD JUST A LITTLE AT A TIME AND TASTE AS YOU GO.

If you have ever been to Italy, you will realise that the simplest dishes can be the best. It's all about the produce, so look for the best-quality beef and the freshest, most peppery rocket and enjoy this delicious, classic dish.

BEEF CARPACCIO
WITH WALNUT OIL

246 calories | 17.3g fat | 3.9g saturates | 0.8g sugar | 0.1g salt | 21.6g protein | 0.6g fibre

Serves 4 as a starter

400g beef tenderloin
4 tablespoons walnut oil
freshly ground black
    pepper
200g rocket leaves
2 lemons, cut into wedges

Place the beef in the freezer for 30 minutes before you are ready to serve as this will firm it up and make it easier to slice thinly.

Using a very sharp knife, slice the beef as thinly as you can.

Lay each slice of beef on a chopping board, cover with clingfilm and, using a rolling pin, stretch and roll the beef until it is as thin as it will go.

Remove the clingfilm and divide the beef between 4 serving plates. Drizzle each one with a tablespoon of walnut oil and season with a few grinds of black pepper. Serve with rocket and lemon wedges on the side.

 TIP BEEF IS PROTEIN-RICH AND CRITICAL FOR MUSCLE GROWTH AND RECOVERY. IT ALSO CONTAINS HIGH AMOUNTS OF IRON AND VITAMIN B12, WHICH BOOST THE IMMUNE SYSTEM AND KEEP THE RED BLOOD CELLS HEALTHY.

Ceviche is the classic South American way to prepare raw fish. It is marinated in citrus juices and the acidity cures the fish, which has the same effect as cooking it, but in a way that preserves all its fresh flavour.

SCALLOP CEVICHE
WITH FRESH HERBS

180 calories | 11.9g fat | 1.8g saturates | 1.6g sugar | 0.3g salt | 14.7g protein | 0.4g fibre

Serves 4

250g fresh raw scallops
juice of 1 lemon
4 tablespoons olive oil
2 spring onions, finely
  chopped
½ small red onion, finely
  chopped
1 red bird's eye chilli,
  finely chopped (seeds
  removed if you don't
  want it hot)
a handful of coriander
  leaves, to garnish
6–8 fresh basil leaves,
  thinly sliced
freshly ground black
  pepper

Using a sharp knife, slice each scallop into about 3 thin discs. Arrange these in a single layer on a large serving plate.

In a bowl, mix together the lemon juice and olive oil. Add the spring onion, onion and chilli and stir to combine.

Pour the dressing over the scallops and set aside to marinate for at least 20 minutes. Scatter over the fresh coriander and basil and season with a few grinds of black pepper.

 TIP AS THE FISH HERE IS NOT COOKED WITH HEAT, IT IS ESSENTIAL THAT YOU USE FISH THAT IS AS FRESH AS POSSIBLE AND WORK WITH VERY CLEAN HANDS, UTENSILS AND SURFACES.

I first made this pâté to go on toasted bread, but discovered it's just as good with fresh, crunchy vegetables. Serve this with carrot and celery crudités for a light lunch or as a great way to start a dinner party.

TUNA AND
OLIVE PATÉ

314 calories | 16.8g fat | 2.3g saturates | 0.4g sugar | 2.7g salt | 40.2g protein | 2g fibre

Serves 4

3 x 185g tins of tuna in
  water, drained
1 tablespoon capers
1 tablespoon chopped
  tarragon
12 fresh basil leaves,
  plus extra to garnish
1 x 50g tin of anchovies,
  drained
150g pitted black olives,
  drained
1 tablespoon Dijon
  mustard
juice of ½ lemon
3 tablespoons olive oil

Place all the ingredients in a food processor and blend until smooth.

Divide the pâté mix between 4 ramekin dishes and refrigerate for at least 30 minutes.

Garnish with fresh basil and serve with freshly chopped carrot and celery crudités.

 TIP TARRAGON IS RICH IN VITAMIN C AND HELPS BOOST THE IMMUNE SYSTEM. IT IS A GREAT HERB TO HAVE ON HAND AND GOES PARTICULARLY WELL WITH MANY TYPES OF FISH (SEE THE RECIPE FOR TUNA WITH OLIVE TAPENADE ON PAGE 119).

This is the kind of meal you get in the Florida Keys – sitting at an old bar on the water, enjoying a beer and a cheap, simple meal of fresh seafood. I know beer is not allowed on the Paleo diet, but this recipe is to enjoy with friends, al fresco.

STEAMED CLAMS

WITH LEMON AND HERBS

328 calories | 12.3g fat | 2.3g saturates | 0.2g sugar | 2.8g salt | 45.5g protein | 0g fibre

Serves 4

6 dozen clams
4 garlic cloves, chopped
50ml vegetable stock
2 tablespoons olive oil
4 tablespoons shredded
   fresh basil
2 tablespoons chopped
   flat-leaf parsley
juice of 1 lemon
freshly ground black
   pepper

Clean your clams in a colander and rinse well. Add to a large stockpot with the garlic and stock, bring to a boil and cover. Cook for 4–5 minutes over a medium heat or until the clams open. Discard any that remain closed.

Add the oil, herbs and lemon juice. Mix in well, season with black pepper and serve.

 TIP CLAMS ARE A GREAT LEAN PROTEIN AS AN 85G SERVING CONTAINS 20G PROTEIN AND ONLY 2G FAT. THIS IS ABOUT THE SAME AS CHICKEN, THOUGH CLAMS ARE FAR MORE NUTRIENT-RICH.

The key to making this dish great is to use the best crab you can. If you are using tinned, you will find you have about three options in the supermarket in terms of cost and quality and I'd recommend you buy the most expensive, as it really makes a difference to the end result here.

ASIAN FUSION
CRAB CAKES

372 calories | 29.2g fat | 4.2g saturates | 1.4g sugar | 1.3g salt | 25.7g protein | 0.9g fibre

Serves 4

1 red bird's eye chilli
1 garlic clove, peeled
½ small onion
a handful of coriander,
  plus extra to garnish
1 tablespoon almond
  flour
1 egg, plus 1 egg white
450g fresh crab meat (or
  premium tinned)
1 tablespoon sesame oil
juice of 1 lime or lemon
freshly ground black
  pepper
3–4 tablespoons olive oil
100g rocket leaves

for the dressing
juice of ½ lemon
3 tablespoons olive oil
a few grinds of black
  pepper

Place the chilli, garlic, onion, coriander, almond flour, egg and egg white in a food processor and blend until smooth.

Transfer this spice and herb mix to a large bowl and add three-quarters of the crab meat, along with the sesame oil and lime or lemon juice. Season with black pepper and stir thoroughly to combine. (Don't be tempted to place all the ingredients in the food processor, as otherwise the fish cakes will have no texture and you'll miss the wonderful flakes of crab.) Add the remaining crab meat and stir into the mixture.

Divide the mixture into 4 portions. On a clean surface, carefully shape into 4 cakes about 2.5cm thick. Transfer to a plate, cover and chill for 30 minutes (or up to a day).

Meanwhile, mix the dressing ingredients together and set aside.

Heat the olive oil in a large, non-stick sauté pan over a high heat, and cook the fish cakes for 2–3 minutes on each side.

Serve with rocket leaves, a scattering of chopped coriander and a drizzle of the lemon and olive oil dressing.

I first realised this recipe was a winner for kids when I made it for my eldest daughter, Eleanor. She loved it instantly and I've made it for her and her friends over and over again. You might want to reduce the chilli quantity a little for a younger crowd, but I guarantee you it will be a hit.

SALMON

FISH CAKES

444 calories | 29.4g fat | 5.1g saturates | 1.8g sugar | 0.4g salt | 43.1g protein | 1.1g fibre

Serves 4

800g salmon fillets, roughly chopped
1 red chilli, roughly chopped
2 spring onions, finely chopped
½ red onion, finely chopped
juice of 1 lime or ½ lemon
1 egg
1 x 2.5cm piece of fresh ginger, grated
a handful of coriander leaves, plus extra to garnish
2 tablespoons olive oil
100g spinach leaves
1 lemon, cut into wedges

Place the salmon, chilli, spring onion, red onion, lime or lemon juice, egg, ginger and coriander in a food processor and blitz together, making sure you retain a little texture.

Divide the fish cake mixture into 4 portions. On a clean surface, carefully shape into 4 cakes about 2.5cm thick. Transfer to a plate, cover and chill for 30 minutes (or up to a day).

Heat the olive oil in a large, non-stick sauté pan over a high heat, and cook the fish cakes for 2–3 minutes on each side.

Serve with spinach leaves, a scattering of chopped coriander and a squeeze of lemon.

 TIP WILD SALMON IS ALWAYS PREFERABLE TO FARMED SALMON AS THE LATTER MAY HAVE BEEN INJECTED WITH ANTIBIOTICS AND COLOUR-ENHANCING CHEMICALS.

Mushrooms have such a meaty texture and are so substantial that you won't even notice this is a vegetarian dish. The almond flour adds a lovely crunch and texture but keeps it tasting light and fresh – a perfect quick and easy lunch.

PORTOBELLO MUSHROOMS WITH ALMOND CRUST

629 calories | 58.2g fat | 5.7g saturates | 4.7g sugar | 0.1g salt | 19.2g protein | 6.8g fibre

Serves 2

4 portobello mushrooms, stems cut out
75g almonds
75g almond flour
a few sprigs of flat-leaf parsley, plus extra to garnish
1 garlic clove, peeled
3 tablespoons olive oil
freshly ground black pepper
150g mixed salad leaves
1 lemon, cut into wedges

Preheat the oven to 240°C/gas mark 9.

Wipe the mushrooms clean with a paper towel (do not use water as this will make them slimy).

In a food processor, blend the almonds, almond flour, parsley and garlic. Transfer this mixture to a wide, shallow bowl, add 2 tablespoons of the olive oil, season and mix together well.

Dip the top of each mushroom into the almond mix, pressing down to coat well, then place on a baking tray. Divide the rest of the mixture between each mushroom and drizzle the remaining olive oil on top.

Bake in the oven for 15–18 minutes, until the almond crust is crispy and golden.

Serve on a pile of salad leaves with a wedge of lemon and an extra sprinkling of chopped parsley.

There are so many restaurants that serve calamari and so often it's deep-fried, greasy and high in saturated fat. However, it doesn't have to be that way and this recipe gives you a lighter, better-tasting version with far less fat. You can also try it with fish fillets – equally tasty!

LIGHT FRIED
CALAMARI

349 calories | 22.3g fat | 3g saturates | 0.7g sugar | 0.6g salt | 34g protein | 1.5g fibre

Serves 4

800g cleaned squid, cut
   into rings
4 tablespoons almond
   flour
freshly ground black
   pepper
4 tablespoons olive oil
1 lemon, cut into wedges

Place the squid in a large ziplock bag, add the flour and a few grinds of black pepper, and shake well so there is a light coating on all the squid. Do this in batches, if you like.

Heat 1 tablespoon of the oil in a large pan over a high heat and add a quarter of the squid. Cook for a minute, then reduce the heat to medium and toss the squid for another 2–3 minutes – turning it over and over until golden brown. Remove the squid and set aside. Repeat in 3 further batches until you have cooked all the squid.

Serve the calamari with a lemon wedge on the side.

 TIP CALAMARI IS ONE OF THE LEANEST AND MOST DELICIOUS TYPES OF SEA-DERIVED PROTEIN, PLUS IT'S OFTEN ONE OF THE CHEAPEST, TOO.

Tahini is a Middle-Eastern ingredient: a thick paste made from ground sesame seeds that is traditionally added to hummus. However, as chickpeas are not part of the Paleo plan, I've created the next best thing and matched sesame seeds with aubergines. You can try this with acorn squash, too, but don't forget the garlic – it's a must.

AUBERGINE
TAHINI DIP

337 calories | 30.5g fat | 4.9g saturates | 9.2g sugar | 0.2g salt | 6.3g protein | 9.9g fibre

Serves 4

2 large aubergines, halved
6 tablespoons olive oil
freshly ground black pepper
6 tablespoons sesame seeds
2 garlic cloves, peeled
freshly chopped flat-leaf parsley, to garnish
300g carrots, peeled and cut into sticks
300g celery, cut into sticks

Preheat the oven to 190°C/gas mark 5.

Prick the aubergines with a fork and place, cut-side up, on a roasting tray. Drizzle with 1 tablespoon of the olive oil and bake in the oven for 20 minutes until the skin is charred and the flesh is soft.

When the aubergine is cooked, scoop out the flesh and place in a food processor. Add the remaining ingredients (except the crudités), along with the rest of the olive oil and blend until smooth.

Scoop the dip into a bowl, sprinkle over some chopped parsley and serve with crunchy celery and carrot crudités.

 TIP TAHINI – GROUND SESAME SEEDS – IS A STAR INGREDIENT, CONTAINING MORE PROTEIN THAN MILK AND MOST NUTS. IT'S ALSO A RICH SOURCE OF B VITAMINS THAT BOOST ENERGY AND BRAIN FUNCTION, AND IMPORTANT MINERALS SUCH AS MAGNESIUM, IRON AND CALCIUM.

 VARIATION TAHINI ALSO MAKES A LOVELY DRESSING FOR SALADS AND GRILLED MEATS. MIX 3 TABLESPOONS TAHINI WITH 2 TABLESPOONS WATER, 1 TABLESPOON LEMON JUICE AND 1/2 CLOVE CRUSHED GARLIC.

Being on a diet doesn't mean you can't snack. You can never eat enough vegetables and these dips just make them a little more interesting. Enjoy as much and as often as you like!

CRUDITÉS WITH SUN-DRIED TOMATO AND OLIVE OIL DIPS

570 calories | 54.7g fat | 8g saturates | 10.6g sugar | 1.4g salt | 7.7g protein | 7.1g fibre

Serves 4

300g carrots, peeled and
  cut into sticks
300g celery, cut into
  sticks
300g raw broccoli florets
300g cherry tomatoes

for the tomato dip
180g sun-dried tomatoes
  in olive oil
1 garlic clove, crushed
2 tablespoons chopped
  basil
5 tablespoons olive oil

for the olive oil dip
2 egg yolks
6 tablespoons olive oil
1 tablespoon chopped
  tarragon
1 garlic clove, peeled

Arrange all the vegetables on a large platter.

FOR THE TOMATO DIP:
Drain the tomatoes from the oil they are in as this is too strong in flavour. Place them in a blender with the remaining ingredients and blend until smooth. Scoop into a serving dish and serve with the vegetables.

FOR THE OLIVE OIL DIP:
Place the egg yolks in a blender and start the motor. Slowly add the oil as a trickle – as you would when making a mayonnaise – and gradually incorporate it all. Add the tarragon and garlic and blitz until smooth. Serve in a dish by the side of the vegetables.

 TIP MYTH HAS IT THAT CELERY IS JUST WATER – IT'S NOT! IT ALSO CONTAINS A UNIQUE COMBINATION OF DISEASE-PREVENTING VITAMINS, MINERALS AND PHYTOCHEMICALS. HOWEVER, IT IS TRUE THAT IT IS VIRTUALLY CALORIE-FREE: 1 STICK CONTAINS 1G FIBRE AND ABOUT 10 CALORIES!

This is a great crowd-pleasing canapé to make for a drinks party. Serve this while dinner is being made and your guests will love it.

SPICY GUACAMOLE
BLINIS

435 calories | 38g fat | 5.4g saturates | 1.7g sugar | 0.1g salt | 14.7g protein | 16.1g fibre

Serves 12

for the blinis
200g almond flour
480g flaxseed flour
2 eggs, beaten
200ml water
2 tablespoons olive oil

for the guacamole
3 large ripe avocados,
  halved and stoned
a handful of fresh
  coriander, chopped,
  plus extra to garnish
2 large tomatoes,
  deseeded and chopped
4 tablespoons olive oil
1 small bird's eye
  chilli, finely chopped
juice of 1 lemon or lime

a few chives, chopped,
  to garnish

First make the blinis. In a large mixing bowl, stir together the flours, egg and water to make a batter.

Heat the oil in a non-stick frying pan over a medium heat and, in batches, drop spoonfuls of the batter into the hot pan to make blini-style pancakes. Cook until the surface starts to bubble (1–2 minutes) and then flip over to cook the other side. Set aside to cool on a plate.

Now make the guacamole. Spoon the avocado flesh into a mixing bowl and mash with a fork. Add the coriander and all the remaining guacamole ingredients and mash together to thoroughly combine.

Spoon a little guacamole onto each blini and top with a scattering of fresh chives and extra coriander.

 TIP FLAXSEEDS ARE INCREDIBLY NUTRITIOUS – RICH IN FIBRE, OMEGA-3 FATTY ACIDS AND ESSENTIAL NUTRIENTS. HOWEVER, WHEN GROUND INTO FLOUR, THEY'RE EASIER TO DIGEST AND SO ARE EVEN BETTER FOR YOU!

We all get cravings for pizza, so here is the best Paleo-friendly way to satisfy them. Sometimes the simplest toppings are the best and here, you'll see, a delicious cheese-free pesto is all you need.

PESTO

PIZZA

416 calories | 40.8g fat | 5g saturates | 1.4g sugar | 0.1g salt | 10g protein | 2.7g fibre

Serves 4

100g almond flour
2 eggs
90ml water
3 tablespoons olive oil

for the topping
4 tablespoons olive oil
1 garlic clove, peeled
a large handful of basil
 leaves
80g pine nuts

Preheat the oven to 190°C/gas mark 5.

In a large mixing bowl, whisk the almond flour, eggs, water and olive oil together. When the mixture starts to resemble a dough, use your hands to knead a little, but be gentle as this will crumble more than normal flour dough.

To make the pesto topping, combine the oil, garlic, basil and pine nuts in a blender and blitz until smooth.

Divide the dough mixture in two and, using your hands rather than a rolling pin, flatten out into 2 pizza shapes on greaseproof paper or on 2 non-stick pizza pans. Top with the pesto, spreading the sauce out almost to the edges.

Cook the pizzas in the oven for 12 minutes, then turn off the heat and finish off for a further 3–4 minutes.

Be creative with your choice of toppings – olives are great on pizzas and so is fish and seafood. The Italians are pretty strict on their 'no cheese with fish' rule and so Neptune pizzas are traditionally cheese-free anyway.

BLACK OLIVE
PIZZA

465 calories | 46.3g fat | 5.8g saturates | 1.2g sugar | 1.3g salt | 10g protein | 6.2g fibre

Serves 4

100g almond flour
2 eggs
90ml water
3 tablespoons olive oil

for the topping
1 x 350g tin of black
   pitted olives, drained
1 garlic clove, peeled
a handful of basil
   leaves
1 tablespoon pine nuts
2 tablespoons olive oil

Preheat the oven to 190°C/gas mark 5.

In a large mixing bowl, whisk the almond flour, eggs, water and olive oil together. When the mixture starts to resemble a dough, use your hands to knead a little, but be gentle as this will crumble more than normal flour dough.

Place all the topping ingredients in a blender and blend to a chunky consistency.

Divide the dough mixture in two and, using your hands rather than a rolling pin, flatten out into 2 pizza shapes on greaseproof paper or on 2 non-stick pizza pans. Top with the olive mixture, spreading it out almost to the edges.

Cook the pizzas in the oven for 12 minutes, then turn off the heat and finish off for a further 3–4 minutes.

I love when I create a healthy dish that doesn't feel 'diet' at all, and this is one of those – pure decadence. I always remember being taken to a very expensive restaurant in New York and inhaling the aroma, which filled the entire place, when white truffles were being shaved over pasta.

GRILLED ARTICHOKES
WITH WHITE TRUFFLE MAYO

260 calories | 26.3g fat | 4.3g saturates | 1.1g sugar | 0g salt | 4.6g protein | 1g fibre

Serves 4

4 large globe artichoke
   hearts, trimmed and
   halved
4 tablespoons olive oil
1 garlic clove, crushed
1 tablespoon chopped
   fresh mixed herbs, like
   rosemary and thyme
1 lemon, cut into wedges

for the truffle mayo
3 egg yolks
4 tablespoons white
   truffle oil

Place the artichokes in a large saucepan of boiling water and simmer over a medium heat for 20 minutes.

Combine the olive oil, garlic and herbs in a small bowl and set aside to infuse.

Meanwhile, make the truffle mayo dip. This is just like a mayonnaise, so place the egg yolks in a bowl and whisk with an electric whisk as you drizzle in the truffle oil. Very slowly incorporate it all so it thickens.

Drain the artichokes and place on paper towels to absorb any water. Now heat a griddle pan (or the barbecue) and lightly brush the artichokes with the infused garlic and herb oil. Cook for 3–5 minutes on each side.

Serve with the white truffle mayonnaise and lemon wedges to squeeze over.

 TIP ARTICHOKES ARE PACKED WITH ANTIOXIDANTS, MAKING THEM INCREDIBLE DEFENDERS AGAINST CANCER, AGEING, HEART DISEASE AND ILLNESS.

One Christmas, I was experimenting with trying to cook parsnips in a different way and I came up with this recipe. Now I eat parsnip purée all year round. It's especially good served under seared scallops with a red wine reduction. Not strictly Paleo, but perfect for a treat day.

PARSNIP PURÉE

489 calories | 36.3g fat | 5.3g saturates | 16.5g sugar | 0.1g salt | 5.4g protein | 18.4g fibre

Serves 2

1 whole head of garlic
6 tablespoons olive oil,
   plus extra for drizzling
6 large parsnips, peeled

Preheat the oven to 240°C/gas mark 9.

Peel away the outer layers of the garlic head, leaving the skin of the individual bulbs intact. With a sharp knife, slice the very top off the garlic head, then wrap it in a piece of foil, leaving an opening at the top. Drizzle 1 tablespoon of the olive oil over the head and seal tightly. Roast in the oven for 40 minutes (or until the cloves feel soft and squishy).

Fill a saucepan with water and bring it to the boil. Slice each parsnip into 4–5 pieces and then cook over a medium heat for 20 minutes.

Drain the parsnips, transfer to a food processor and add the remaining olive oil.

Take the roasted garlic out of the oven and allow to cool slightly. Squeeze about half of the garlic cloves out of their skin and place in the food processor. Blitz until smooth.

To serve, spoon the purée onto plates, drizzle with a little oil and accompany with a few of the roasted garlic cloves on the side.

 TIP ROASTED GARLIC IS DELICIOUS AS THE LONG COOKING PROCESS REDUCES ITS PUNGENCY, MAKING IT SWEET, STICKY AND GOLDEN, WITH THE TEXTURE OF BUTTER.

This dish is great as a side to go with any Red recipe.
Red onions take on a wonderful sweet flavour when cooked and
I love to contrast this with the addition of fresh green herbs.

CARAMELISED ONIONS

249 calories| 11.4g fat | 1.6g saturates | 32.5g sugar | trace salt | 2.3g protein | 3.3g fibre

Serves 4

4 tablespoons olive oil
6 red onions, finely sliced
50ml vegetable stock
6 tablespoons raw honey
freshly ground black
   pepper
chopped fresh herbs
   (flat-leaf parsley
   and thyme work
   particularly well)

Heat 2 tablespoons of the oil in a large, non-stick frying pan over a high heat. Add the onions and cook, tossing continuously, for 2–3 minutes. Add the remaining olive oil and cook for a further 3–4 minutes, until the onion has turned a dark, rich brown colour (this is the sugar in the onion caramelising).

Add the stock and honey to the pan and reduce the temperature to low. Cook for 5–6 minutes until the liquid has absorbed and the onions have caramelised.

Season with a few grinds of black pepper and increase the heat for a final few minutes.

Stir through the fresh herbs and serve immediately.

When I tried out this tempura for the book, I was so happy with the results that I immediately shared the recipe with friends. I also recommend that you try it with other vegetables, like aubergine or carrot, and king prawns too.

CRISPY VEGETABLE
TEMPURA

199 calories | 17.7g fat | 8.4g saturates | 2.2g sugar | 0.1g salt | 7.3g protein | 2.4g fibre

Serves 6

6–8 large courgettes,
   topped and tailed
100g almond flour
6 tablespoons almond or
   coconut oil, for frying
3 eggs

Slice your courgettes into thin strips and pat with kitchen paper to remove any moisture – they must be completely dry. Set aside.

Place the almond flour on a large serving plate and set aside. Heat the oil in a large wok to 190°C.

Whisk the eggs in a large bowl and then dip in the courgettes, about 3–4 slices at a time.

Now dip the courgettes in the almond flour, ensuring they are thoroughly coated.

In batches, fry the courgette slices in the hot oil for 2–3 minutes until golden and puffy. Drain on kitchen paper and continue to work through the remaining tempura.

Season with pepper and serve.

 TIP DON'T BE TEMPTED TO USE OLIVE OIL AS IT'S NOT GOOD FOR FRYING AT HIGH TEMPERATURES. ALMOND OR COCONUT OILS ARE BETTER FOR THIS PURPOSE.

We always remember how much we love Brussels sprouts at Christmas time but, in my view, it's criminal to neglect them throughout the rest of the year. This is my favourite way to cook them, as the dish is full of great texture and the sprouts never become mushy.

ROASTED BRUSSELS SPROUTS WITH CHESTNUTS

455 calories | 29.3g fat | 4.5g saturates | 10.9g sugar | 0.1g salt | 12g protein | 13.3g fibre

Serves 6

800g Brussels sprouts, trimmed
1 x 450g tin of chestnuts, quartered
60g unsalted cashew nuts, roughly chopped
1 red onion, peeled and quartered
4 tablespoons almond oil
1 tablespoon olive oil
60g unsalted walnuts
60g toasted pumpkin seeds
freshly ground black pepper

Preheat the oven to 230°C/gas mark 8.

Place all the ingredients in a large mixing bowl, toss together and season with black pepper.

Tip everything into a roasting pan and roast in the oven for 20–25 minutes, tossing thoroughly halfway through the cooking time.

TIP THIS IS A GREAT DISH SERVED ON ITS OWN AS A VEGETARIAN LUNCH. FEEL FREE TO ADD A FEW EXTRA PECANS OR CASHEWS TO THE CHESTNUTS.

VARIATION I ALSO LOVE ROASTING CARROTS AND PARSNIPS TOGETHER WITH A LITTLE OLIVE OIL, A FEW SPRIGS OF ROSEMARY AND A LIGHT DRIZZLE OF HONEY. COOK AS ABOVE BUT FOR SLIGHTLY LONGER – ABOUT 40 MINUTES, TOSSING EVERY 10 MINUTES OR SO.

This is a great side dish with any mains that are marked Red.
Spinach is a great source of iron and the coconut milk gives this a similar
texture to creamed spinach.

COCONUT SPINACH
WITH CHOPPED ALMONDS

111 calories | 9.2g fat | 2.2g saturates | 2g sugar | 0.4g salt | 4.5g protein | 2.8g fibre

Serves 4

1 tablespoon olive oil
400g spinach
4–6 tablespoons light
  coconut milk
2 tablespoons roughly
  chopped almonds
freshly ground black
  pepper

Heat the olive oil in a large pan over a high heat and add the spinach.
Fry for 2–3 minutes, stirring constantly.

Add the coconut milk and simmer for 2 minutes, then add the almonds,
stir through and serve with a twist of black pepper.

SOUPS & SALADS

Chilled soups are wonderfully refreshing and so perfect for a hot summer's day or even after a hard day at the office when you want something light and simple in the evening. The creaminess of the avocado gives this soup a wonderful texture – try it!

CHILLED AVOCADO
SOUP

313 calories | 30g fat | 6.3g saturates | 0.8g sugar | 0.1g salt | 7.8g protein | 6.8g fibre

Serves 4

4 ripe avocados, halved and stoned
400ml cold vegetable stock
100g salmon roe (optional)
2 tablespoons chopped chives
freshly ground black pepper

Scoop the avocado flesh into a food processor, add the cold vegetable stock and blend until smooth. Chill the soup in the refrigerator for at least 30 minutes.

Divide the chilled soup between 4 bowls and serve with a scoop of salmon roe (if using), a scattering of chopped chives and a twist of black pepper.

 TIP IF YOU ARE WATCHING YOUR WEIGHT AND YOUR FAT INTAKE, REDUCE THE AMOUNT OF AVOCADO BY HALF. THE TEXTURE WILL BE LESS CREAMY BUT THE FLAVOUR WILL STILL BE THERE.

This soup can be served hot or cold. Serving it cold has a similar taste to a French Vichyssoise – a thick soup made of puréed leeks, potatoes and cream. In fact, you can pan-fry a little shredded leek for a few minutes and add to the soup as a garnish.

ASPARAGUS
SOUP

90 calories | 6.4g fat | 0.9g saturates | 3.3g sugar | 0g salt | 4.1g protein | 2.7g fibre

Serves 4

2 tablespoons olive oil
1 onion, finely chopped
400g asparagus, trimmed
500ml vegetable stock
a handful of chives,
   chopped
freshly ground black
   pepper

Heat the oil in a large saucepan and sauté the onion over a medium heat for 3–5 minutes.

Chop each asparagus spear into 3 and add to the pan with the onion, sautéing for 2–3 minutes. Add the stock and simmer for 12–15 minutes.

Turn off the heat and allow to cool slightly before blending the soup with a hand blender until smooth.

Return the soup to a saucepan and place back on a medium heat to warm through.

Serve with a sprinkling of fresh chives and a twist or two of freshly ground black pepper.

 TIP THE SEASON FOR FRESH ASPARAGUS IS VERY SHORT, SO MAKE SURE YOU MAKE THE MOST OF IT BY COOKING THIS INCREDIBLY FLAVOURSOME SOUP.

This soup is not quite as simple as the other ones in this chapter, but it is worth every effort. I often make double quantities and freeze a batch. That way, you can also use it as a stock for cooking a quick seafood or fish supper.

FISH SOUP OR FRENCH
BOUILLABAISSE

182 calories | 10g fat | 1.6g saturates | 1.4g sugar | 1.8g salt | 20.3g protein | 0.4g fibre

Serves 6

3 tablespoons olive oil
2 garlic cloves, finely chopped
900ml fish stock
4 tablespoons tomato paste
4 tablespoons sun-dried tomato paste
200g skinless salmon fillet, cut into chunks
200g skinless monkfish fillet, cut into chunks
15 small scallops
16 tiger shrimp, peeled
20 clams
20 mussels
a handful of chives, chopped
freshly ground black pepper

Heat the oil in a large saucepan over a medium heat and fry the garlic for 30 seconds. Add the stock and tomato pastes and bring to a simmer. Cover with a lid and simmer gently for 15 minutes.

Add all the fish and seafood and cook, uncovered, for 4–5 minutes, or until the fish is cooked and the clams and mussels have opened. Discard any shells that remain closed.

Serve with a scattering of chives and a twist of black pepper.

 TIP SCALLOPS ARE ALMOST 80% PROTEIN, PLUS THEY'RE A RICH SOURCE OF VITAMIN B12, MAGNESIUM, POTASSIUM AND MANY OTHER NUTRIENTS.

A traditional French onion soup is served with a toasted slice
of baguette smothered in Gruyère and, while very tasty, is neither healthy
nor part of the Paleo plan! However, this recipe is both those things, plus
it retains all the flavour and restorative umami of the French classic.

ONION AND THYME

SOUP

150 calories | 9.1g fat | 1.2g saturates | 9.6g sugar | 0.2g salt | 4g protein | 3.3g fibre

Serves 4

3 tablespoons olive oil
4 large onions, peeled
    and finely sliced
approx. 1 tablespoon
    fresh thyme leaves
3 garlic cloves, crushed
1 bay leaf
1 litre good-quality
    vegetable stock
chopped flat-leaf parsley,
    to garnish
freshly ground black
    pepper

In a large cast-iron casserole dish or saucepan, heat the oil over a low
heat and gently cook the onion and thyme until the onion is softened
but not browned – about 20 minutes. Increase the heat slightly and
cook for 15 minutes, until the onion becomes dark golden, sticky and
caramelised, stirring now and again to stop it catching. Add the garlic
and cook, stirring, for a few minutes.

Add the bay leaf and stock and bring to the boil. Season and simmer
for 15 minutes. Serve with a scattering of fresh parsley and a twist
of black pepper.

TIP FOUR MAY SEEM LIKE A LOT, BUT COOKING THE ONIONS FOR THIS
LENGTH OF TIME MEANS THAT THEY LOSE THEIR PUNGENCY – I PROMISE!

TIP FOR THIS SOUP, MAKE SURE YOU HAVE A REALLY GOOD-QUALITY
VEGETABLE STOCK AS IT WILL MAKE ALL THE DIFFERENCE TO THE
SOUP'S DEPTH OF FLAVOUR.

The key to this soup is to include a really good mix of mushrooms. Shiitake mushrooms are always great, but you can use almost anything, from small button mushrooms through to soaked, dried porcini – the latter always provide an excellent depth of flavour.

MIXED MUSHROOM
SOUP

159 calories | 14g fat | 5.8g saturates | 2.9g sugar | 0.2g salt | 3.8g protein | 2.2g fibre

Serves 4

2 tablespoons olive oil
1 white onion, finely
   chopped
400g mixed mushrooms,
   sliced
3 garlic cloves, crushed
600ml vegetable stock
200ml light coconut milk
finely chopped flat-leaf
   parsley, to garnish
freshly ground black
   pepper

Heat the oil in a saucepan over a high heat and sweat the onion for 3–4 minutes. Add all the mushrooms, reduce the heat and cook, stirring, for a further few minutes.

Add the garlic and stock and simmer for 15 minutes, then add the coconut milk and cook for another minute to fuse the flavours.

Turn off the heat and allow to cool slightly, before blending the soup with a hand blender until smooth.

Return the soup to a saucepan and place back on a medium heat to warm through.

Serve with a sprinkling of fresh parsley and a twist of black pepper.

 TIP MUSHROOMS ARE INCREASINGLY BEING HAILED AS A SUPERFOOD – THEY CONTAIN VIRTUALLY NO FAT, SUGAR OR SALT, PLUS THEY'RE A GOOD SOURCE OF DIETARY FIBRE AS WELL AS ALL FIVE B VITAMINS.

Coconut and beetroot might seem like a surprising combination but trust me, it works. The finished soup is also a wonderful colour – a beautiful, vibrant pink – so I find it's a great way to start a dinner party.

COCONUT BEETROOT
SOUP

219 calories | 15.8g fat | 9.8g saturates | 11.7g sugar | 0.2g salt | 4.7g protein | 3.9g fibre

Serves 4

500g beetroot
3 bay leaves
few sprigs of oregano
2 tablespoons olive oil
1 red onion, finely
   chopped
700ml vegetable stock
400ml light coconut milk
freshly ground black
   pepper
finely chopped flat-leaf
   parsley, to garnish

Cook the beetroot in boiling salted water with the bay leaves and oregano for 50–60 minutes. Take off the heat and let cool in the water. When cool enough to handle, peel and roughly chop.

Heat the olive oil in a large saucepan over a medium heat and sweat the onion for 3–4 minutes. Add the beetroot and toss in the oil. Add the stock and simmer, covered, for 15 minutes. Add the coconut milk and simmer, uncovered, for 2–3 minutes. Season with black pepper and take off the heat.

Transfer to a blender and purée until smooth. Return to a pan and warm through.

Spoon into serving bowls and finish with a scattering of fresh parsley.

 TIP BEETROOT HAS A MEDIUM GI (GLYCAEMIC INDEX) OF 64 BUT A VERY LOW GL (GLYCAEMIC LOAD) OF 2.9, WHICH MEANS IT'S CONVERTED INTO SUGARS VERY SLOWLY AND THEREFORE KEEPS BLOOD SUGAR LEVELS NICE AND STABLE.

Pumpkin is a starchy form of carbohydrate, but much less so than potato, sweet potato or yams, so it is fine in moderation. I find it a wonderful ingredient for soup, as it creates a rich, thick texture but with a lovely, delicate sweetness.

ROASTED PUMPKIN
SOUP

173 calories | 14.6g fat | 7.2g saturates | 5.2g sugar | 0.2g salt | 3.2g protein | 2.8g fibre

Serves 6

1 medium pumpkin
7 tablespoons olive oil
1 whole head of garlic
1 onion, finely chopped
1.1 litres vegetable stock
400ml light coconut milk
4 tablespoons pumpkin
   seeds
fresh thyme leaves, to
   garnish (optional)

Preheat the oven to 220°C/gas mark 7.

Cut the top off the pumpkin, scoop out the seeds and fibres and discard. Cut the pumpkin into 4 quarters and place on a baking tray. Drizzle over 4 tablespoons of the olive oil.

Slice the top off the head of the garlic and drizzle over 1 tablespoon of the olive oil. Wrap in foil (so it is completely sealed), place on the baking tray with the pumpkin and then roast in the hot oven for 45 minutes.

Heat 1 tablespoon of the olive oil in a large saucepan and gently fry the onion for a few minutes. Add the vegetable stock and bring to a simmer, then cover and take off the heat.

When the pumpkin is cooked, discard the skin and add the flesh to the saucepan. Squeeze the garlic flesh out of the skins and add to the pot, along with the coconut milk. Bring the contents to the boil and cook for 10 minutes on a medium heat.

Remove the pan from the heat and set aside to cool slightly before puréeing the soup in a food processor until velvety and smooth.

Heat the remaining tablespoon oil in a frying pan over a medium heat and fry the pumpkin seeds for 1–2 minutes until just toasted. To serve, reheat the soup and garnish with the toasted pumpkin seeds and fresh thyme leaves, if using.

You often see salmon skin on the menu in Japanese restaurants and, in my opinion, it is far too good a thing to throw away – it crisps up in a pan and adds a wonderful crunch to a salad.

SALMON AND
SALMON SKIN SALAD

633 calories | 53.2g fat | 9.6g saturates | 1.3g sugar | 0.5g salt | 36.1g protein | 3.9g fibre

Serves 4

3 x 230g salmon fillets, skin on
freshly ground black pepper
1 tablespoon olive oil
150g mixed salad leaves
2 ripe avocados, sliced

for the dressing
juice of 2 lemons
1 tablespoon Dijon mustard
6 tablespoons olive oil

Using a sharp knife, separate the salmon from the skin and reserve for later. Cut the skin into strips about 2.5cm wide and slice each salmon fillet into 4. Season both with black pepper.

Place a large non-stick pan over a medium heat and fry the salmon for 3 minutes on each side (salmon is an oily fish, so you shouldn't need to add any extra oil to the pan). Set aside to cool.

In a separate frying pan, heat the olive oil and fry the skin over a high heat for about 4 minutes or until nicely brown.

Mix all the dressing ingredients together and dress the salad leaves and avocado slices in a large bowl. Add the salmon and salmon skin and toss to combine.

 TIP SALMON SKIN IS FATTY, BUT IT'S GOOD FAT SO FULL OF OMEGA-3 FATTY ACIDS NECESSARY FOR HEALTHY BRAIN FUNCTION. OMEGA-3 ALSO HELPS REDUCE INFLAMMATION AND LOWERS THE RISK OF CHRONIC DISEASES SUCH AS HEART DISEASE, CANCER AND ARTHRITIS.

I tasted my first sashimi salad about 10 years ago, when I was in Hong Kong at Tokyo Joe's, and I instantly loved it. These days, you see it on a lot of restaurant menus, but this version is a nice, simple one you can make at home.

SEAWEED AND SASHIMI
SALAD

565 calories | 45.2g fat | 8.1g saturates | 2.3g sugar | 0.2g salt | 36.6g protein | 4.6g fibre

Serves 4

150g mixed salad leaves
(including rocket)
1 avocado, sliced
4 sheets of seaweed
paper, shredded
12 cherry tomatoes,
halved
1 tablespoon olive oil
3 tablespoons sesame
seeds
1 x 300g tuna steak
(sashimi grade; ask
the fish counter),
1 x 300g skinless salmon
fillet

for the dressing
4 tablespoons sesame oil
juice of 1 lemon
1 teaspoon wasabi paste
2 tablespoons olive oil

Place the salad leaves in a bowl with the avocado, shredded seaweed and tomatoes.

Heat the olive oil in a heavy non-stick grill pan. Meanwhile, spread 1 tablespoon of the sesame seeds over a small plate and press the tuna steak into the seeds on all sides to coat. Sear the tuna in the hot pan for 30 seconds on each side. Transfer to a chopping board and, with a sharp knife, slice thinly. Repeat the process, this time using the salmon.

Mix all the ingredients for the dressing and toss into the salad. Add the tuna and salmon and scatter with the remaining sesame seeds.

 TIP SEAWEED IS AN EXCELLENT INGREDIENT FOR CRUMBLING INTO SOUPS, SALADS, STEWS AND STIR FRIES. IT'S FULL OF NUTRIENTS AND VERY LOW IN CALORIES.

Seafood salad is a staple in Italian cuisine. They lightly poach incredibly fresh fish and seafood and then pour over a great-quality olive oil to preserve it. The result melts in your mouth and makes perfect picnic food on a hot summer's day.

ITALIAN SEAFOOD
SALAD

303 calories | 19.9g fat | 3g saturates | 2.1g sugar | 0.8g salt | 25.6g protein | 1.1g fibre

Serves 4

225g scallops
115g medium prawns, shell on
225g mussels
115g cleaned squid, cut into rings
12 pitted Kalamata olives
6 tablespoons lemon juice
6 tablespoons olive oil
1 large garlic clove, finely chopped
1 tablespoon finely chopped flat-leaf parsley
1 tablespoon finely chopped chives
¼ teaspoon chilli flakes
1 lemon, sliced
1 medium red onion, thinly sliced
freshly ground black pepper

Bring a large pot of water to the boil. Add the scallops, prawns, mussels, and squid (calamari) to the boiling water and simmer for 2 minutes, or until the seafood is cooked and the mussel shells open. Drain.

Peel the prawns and remove the meat from the mussel shells. Discard any mussels that remain closed.

Place the seafood in a bowl and add all the remaining ingredients, tossing well. Chill for 30 minutes and serve.

 VARIATION YOU COULD ALSO GIVE THIS DISH AN ORIENTAL TWIST BY USING FRESH CORIANDER, SESAME SEEDS AND SESAME OIL.

Prawns and avocado make a classic combination and this dressing adds an interesting new angle – fresh and citrussy.

TIGER PRAWNS
WITH AVOCADO

472 calories | 20.3g fat | 3.7g saturates | 23.3g sugar | 0.9g salt | 34.8g protein | 1.8g fibre

Serves 4

1 tablespoon olive oil
680g large tiger prawns,
   peeled but with
   heads on
600g mixed salad leaves
2 ripe avocados, peeled,
   stoned and finely
   chopped
freshly ground black
   pepper

for the dressing
juice of 1 orange
4 tablespoons olive oil
1 tablespoon lemon juice
1 tablespoon shredded
   basil
1 teaspoon Dijon
   mustard

Heat the olive oil in a large, non-stick frying pan and fry the prawns for 1–2 minutes on each side or until cooked through. Take off the heat and set aside.

Place the salad leaves in a large mixing bowl and add the avocado.

In a small bowl, mix all the dressing ingredients, then toss into the salad.

Serve the salad topped with the prawns and a grind or two of black pepper.

 TIP PRAWNS ARE HIGH IN NUTRIENTS AND PROTEIN AND LOW IN CALORIES AND FAT – PERFECT FOR WEIGHT LOSS!

I am not always a fan of sweet and sour but this combination works very well. Try to get strawberries that are a little on the firm side as this keeps them from being oversweet.

STRAWBERRY AND SALMON
SALAD WITH MIXED NUTS

638 calories | 49.2g fat | 7.4g saturates | 6.5g sugar | 0.3g salt | 39.6g protein | 3.2g fibre

Serves 4

2 x 300g skinless salmon
   fillets
12 large strawberries,
   thinly sliced
80g cashew nuts,
   chopped
80g almonds, chopped
600g mixed salad leaves
your choice of fresh
   chopped herbs, such as
   chives or mint

for the dressing
4 tablespoons olive oil
juice of ½ lemon
1 tablespoon finely
   chopped chives
1 teaspoon Dijon
   mustard

Heat a dry, non-stick frying pan to a high heat and add the salmon fillets. Cook for 2–3 minutes on each side, then turn the heat down to medium and cook for a further 2–3 minutes. The salmon should release enough oil to cook the fish perfectly. Take off the heat and set aside.

Whisk together the dressing ingredients and set aside. Combine the strawberries with the nuts and salad leaves in a large mixing bowl.

Arrange the salad on a plate and top with the salmon. Dress with the vinaigrette and a scattering of fresh herbs.

 TIP THERE'S NO DAIRY ON THE PALEO PLAN, BUT THERE'S NO NEED TO WORRY ABOUT YOUR CALCIUM INTAKE FOR HEALTHY BONES – ALMONDS ARE VERY CALCIUM-RICH, PLUS THEY ARE FULL OF VITAMIN E, WHICH IS GOOD FOR YOUR SKIN.

The fresh orange and coriander and beautiful, jewel-like pomegranate seeds make this salad a perfect winter pick-me-up – plus it's high in vitamin C to ward off any coughs and sneezes.

CHICKEN, ORANGE AND POMEGRANATE SALAD

364 calories | 15.6g fat | 2.4g saturates | 18.1g sugar | 0.3g salt | 38.3g protein | 5.7g fibre

Serves 4

4 large oranges, peeled
   and thinly sliced
5 tablespoons olive oil
juice of ¼ lemon
a handful of coriander,
   chopped
200g pomegranate seeds
4 skinless chicken
   breasts, cut into strips
freshly ground black
   pepper

Place the orange slices in a large mixing bowl. Add 3 tablespoons of the olive oil, plus the lemon juice, coriander and pomegranate seeds. Toss well to combine and set aside to marinate while you cook the chicken.

Heat the remaining olive oil in a non-stick grill pan and sear the chicken over a high heat for about 3 minutes on each side, or until cooked through. Turn off the heat and set aside to rest for a few minutes.

To serve, divide the salad between 4 serving plates, top with the warm chicken slices and finish with a few grinds of black pepper.

 TIP I LOVE POMEGRANATE SEEDS. THEY'RE JUICY AND BURSTING WITH HEALTH BENEFITS – VITAMINS A, B AND C, FOLIC ACID, FIBRE, POTASSIUM AND CALCIUM.

This meal originated in Nice, France, hence the name, but is now served all around the world. It's nicely versatile, as you can make it with fresh tuna or tinned tuna, or quail's eggs or hen's eggs. It's always a winner, either way.

SALAD

NIÇOISE

531 calories | 36.8g fat | 6.9g saturates | 2.8g sugar | 2.2g salt | 48.2g protein | 2.2g fibre

Serves 4

4 eggs
600g mixed salad
   leaves or 2 cos
   lettuces, trimmed
1 tablespoon olive oil
2 x 300g tuna steaks
12–16 Kalamata olives
1 x 56g tin of anchovies,
   drained

for the dressing
juice of 1 lemon
6 tablespoons olive oil
1 tablespoon Dijon
   mustard
1 tablespoon finely
   chopped tarragon

Place the eggs in a saucepan of boiling water and boil for 5 minutes. Drain and peel. Quarter the eggs and set aside.

Whisk together the dressing ingredients in a small bowl. Place the salad leaves in a large mixing bowl, pour over the dressing and toss well.

Heat the olive oil in a large, non-stick pan over a medium heat and sear the tuna steaks for 1–2 minutes on each side. Take out of the pan and place on a cutting board. Slice thinly.

Divide the salad between 4 bowls and top with the olives, anchovies, eggs and tuna slices.

 TIP FRESH TARRAGON IS A LOVELY ADDITION TO THIS SALAD (PLUS IT PACKS A HEALTHY ANTIOXIDANT PUNCH). FILL YOUR FRIDGE WITH BUNCHES OF FRESH HERBS, AS THEY ADD INTEREST AND FLAVOUR TO ANY KIND OF SALAD.

This is the simplest and easiest of salads to rustle up at a moment's notice. Quail's eggs always add a bit of class, so I often serve this as a dinner party starter.

QUAIL'S EGG AND
PARMA HAM SALAD

349 calories | 28.5g fat | 5.5 g saturates | 3.5g sugar | 2g salt | 21g protein | 2.4g fibre

Serves 4

1 teaspoon olive oil
12 quail's eggs
800g mixed salad leaves
12 slices of Parma ham
freshly ground black
   pepper

for the dressing
4 tablespoons walnut oil
juice of ½ lemon
1 teaspoon Dijon
   mustard

Heat a non-stick frying pan on a medium heat and add the olive oil. Crack the quail's eggs, two at a time, into the pan and fry them as you would a normal fried egg – they only take 20–30 seconds to cook. Remove with a slotted spoon and set aside to cool.

In a small bowl, whisk all the dressing ingredients together. Place the salad leaves in a large salad bowl and toss with the dressing.

Arrange the salad leaves on a plate and top with the Parma ham and fried quail's eggs and a grind or two of black pepper.

 TIP PARMA HAM IS SO FULL OF FLAVOUR THAT YOU DON'T NEED TO USE MUCH. TWO OR THREE WAFER-THIN SLICES ARE QUITE SUFFICIENT AND, IF YOU CUT OFF THE RIND, YOU KEEP THE FAT CONTENT NICE AND LOW.

This Thai beef salad can be served hot or cold. In Thailand, they really spice it up with lots of bird's eye chillies (one of the hottest kinds). However, if you discard the seeds, you take out a lot of the heat.

THAI BEEF

SALAD

258 calories | 9.6g fat | 3.4g saturates | 6.2g sugar | 0.3g salt | 36g protein | 1.1g fibre

Serves 4

2 x 300g lean sirloin
   steaks
1 tablespoon olive oil
   (if frying)
a handful of coriander,
   chopped, plus extra
   to garnish
a handful of mint leaves,
   chopped
2–3 bird's eye chillies,
   finely chopped
1 garlic clove, crushed
juice of 1 lemon
1 x 2cm piece of fresh
   ginger, grated
1 tablespoon honey
8 radishes, thinly sliced
½ cucumber, thinly sliced
1 red onion, thinly sliced
freshly ground black
   pepper

Either grill the steak or fry in the olive oil for 2–3 minutes on each side until nicely browned but still a little pink in the centre. Transfer to a warmed plate and rest for 5 minutes.

In a large bowl, mix together the herbs, chillies, garlic, lemon juice, ginger and honey.

Using a sharp knife, slice the beef into thin strips, and add them to the bowl with the dressing. Set aside to marinate while you prepare the salad.

Arrange the radish, cucumber and red onion on a large serving platter, then top with the beef and spoon over the dressing. Season with black pepper and garnish with a little extra coriander.

 TIP GINGER IS A WONDER SPICE THAT STIMULATES THE APPETITE, AIDS DIGESTION AND HELPS FIGHT OFF COLDS AND FLU.

This salad has wonderful texture – the crispy coated aubergine
that turns soft in the middle, combined with the hard crunch of the chopped
almonds. It makes a perfect lunch or light dinner.

FRIED AUBERGINE
SALAD

465 calories | 40.5g fat | 5.1g saturates | 10.5g sugar | 0.2g salt | 14g protein | 7.6g fibre

Serves 4

2 eggs
4 tablespoons almond
   flour
2–3 tablespoons olive oil
1 large aubergine, sliced
600g mixed salad leaves
2 carrots, peeled and
   grated
12 cherry tomatoes,
   halved

for the dressing
80g toasted almonds,
   roughly chopped
4 tablespoons almond oil
   or olive oil
juice of 1 lemon
a handful of fresh chives,
   chopped, plus extra
   to garnish
1 teaspoon English
   mustard powder

Whisk the eggs in a bowl and place the almond flour on a plate.
Heat the oil in a large, non-stick frying pan over a medium heat.
Dip the aubergine slices in the egg and then in the flour, coating well.

With a slotted spoon, lower the aubergine into the hot oil and fry for
3–4 minutes on each side. You may want to do this in a few batches.
When you put too much food in a pan, it creates moisture and poaches
the food, so do 3–4 slices at a time so you get a good colour on them.

Drain on kitchen paper and continue to work through the rest in
batches.

Mix all the salad dressing ingredients together and dress the salad
leaves in a large mixing bowl. Toss in the tomatoes and carrots.

Arrange the leaves on a plate, top with the fried aubergine and decorate
with a few chives.

 VARIATION ALTERNATIVELY, FRY THE AUBERGINE FOR JUST 1 MINUTE
ON EACH SIDE AND THEN ROAST IN THE OVEN AT 200°C/GAS MARK 6
FOR 20 MINUTES.

Beetroot is a star vegetable – a great source of fibre,
excellent for detox and full of potassium and vitamins B and C.

BEETROOT, JICAMA AND CARROT SALAD

333 calories | 23.4g fat | 3.3g saturates | 18.1g sugar | 0.3g salt | 7.9g protein | 9.4g fibre

Serves 4

juice of ½ orange
juice of ½ lemon
4 tablespoons olive oil
300g carrots, grated
400g beetroot, grated
300g jicama, grated
freshly ground black
   pepper
100g sunflower seeds
chopped fresh coriander

In a small bowl, mix together the orange juice, lemon juice and olive oil.

In a large bowl, mix together the carrot, beetroot and jicama.
Pour over the dressing, season with pepper and toss well.

Serve the salad on a plate with a scattering of sunflower seeds and
some chopped fresh coriander.

 TIP THE JICAMA IS A SWEET ROOT VEGETABLE THAT LOOKS LIKE A
TURNIP. IT'S OFTEN USED IN SOUTH AMERICAN AND ASIAN COOKING
AND PACKS A HEALTHY PUNCH – RICH IN FIBRE, LIKE BEETROOT, AND
HIGH IN VITAMIN C.

TOMATO, CAPER AND RED ONION SALAD

59 calories | 3.2g fat | 0.5g saturates | 6.2g sugar | trace salt | 1.2g protein | 2.2g fibre

Serves 4

4 large tomatoes, sliced
¼ red onion, sliced
1 tablespoon capers
1 tablespoon olive oil
1 tablespoon balsamic
   vinegar

Arrange the tomatoes, red onion and capers on a plate and drizzle with
the olive oil and balsamic vinegar.

 TIP CAPERS ADD INTEREST TO ANY SALAD AND PACK A MIGHTY
ANTIOXIDANT PUNCH. THEY'RE ALSO GREAT WITH MANY FISH DISHES
AND SAUCES.

Papaya is the fruit of the pawpaw tree and, in Asia, is known to help digestion. For this very traditional Thai salad, the trick is to use the under-ripe fruit (green rather than orange) as this gives the salad a wonderful crunch and is the perfect way to eat it.

THAI GREEN
PAPAYA SALAD

176 calories | 7.7g fat | 1.6g saturates | 16.8g sugar | 2.3g salt | 8.1g protein | 3g fibre

Serves 4

1 green papaya,
   grated
12 cherry tomatoes,
   halved
4 tablespoons chopped
   cashew nuts
2 tablespoons dried
   shrimp
freshly ground black
   pepper
a handful of coriander,
   chopped, plus extra
   to garnish

for the dressing
3 garlic cloves, crushed
1 small red chilli, finely
   chopped
2 tablespoons lemon juice
2 tablespoons Red Boat
   fish sauce
2 tablespoons raw honey

Place all the salad ingredients except the coriander in a large bowl and toss to combine.

In a small bowl, combine all the dressing ingredients and whisk. Pour the dressing over the salad and toss again. Season with black pepper, scatter with fresh coriander and serve.

 TIP THE TRADITIONAL THAI DISH HAS PEANUTS AND PALM SUGAR, WHICH I HAVE SWAPPED FOR CASHEWS AND HONEY INSTEAD TO MAKE IT SUITABLE FOR THE PALEO PLAN.

Potatoes contain potentially harmful antinutrients and are therefore not included on the Paleo plan, but butternut squash is the perfect vegetable replacement to satisfy all your carb cravings.

BUTTERNUT SQUASH AND PUMPKIN SEED SALAD

446 calories | 31.3g fat | 4.6g saturates | 17.5g sugar | 0.1g salt | 11.4g protein | 9.3g fibre

Serves 4

1 large butternut squash,
  peeled and cut in half
  (seeds discarded)
2 tablespoons olive oil
1 tablespoon chopped
  thyme
1 tablespoon raw honey,
  melted
600g rocket leaves
120g toasted pumpkin
  seeds
freshly ground black
  pepper

for the dressing
4 tablespoons olive oil
juice of ½ lemon
juice of ½ orange
1 teaspoon Dijon
  mustard
1 teaspoon chopped
  thyme leaves

Preheat the oven to 220°C/gas mark 7.

Chop the butternut squash into wedges and place in a large bowl. Drizzle over the oil, add the thyme and toss to coat. Place on a baking tray and cook in the oven for 30 minutes. Every 10 minutes, remove the baking tray and toss the squash so that all the edges become roasted and caramelised. After 30 minutes, toss one last time, drizzle with the honey, cook for a further 5 minutes, then set aside to cool slightly.

Meanwhile, mix all the dressing ingredients together and dress the rocket leaves in a large bowl. Scatter the pumpkin seeds on top and toss with the butternut squash. Finish with a few grinds of black pepper and serve.

 TIP BUTTERNUT SQUASH HAS A LOVELY SWEET, NUTTY TASTE SO YOU DON'T HAVE TO DO MUCH TO IT. I LOVE TO EAT IT RAW, BUT IT'S REALLY PERFECT ROASTED, WHEN IT CARAMELISES BEAUTIFULLY.

This very simple salad never fails to impress. Figs have a lovely delicate flavour and taste fantastic when they are grilled. Here, the honey brings out all their natural sweetness, while the truffle oil adds a contrasting rich, earthiness – you must try it!

ROASTED FIGS IN
TRUFFLE OIL AND HONEY

171 calories | 8.8g fat | 1.3g saturates | 22.3g sugar | 0.3g salt | 1.6g protein | 2g fibre

Serves 4

12 ripe figs, cut in half
3 tablespoons white
    truffle oil
3 tablespoons raw honey,
    melted
3 tablespoons chopped
    basil
150g rocket leaves

for the vinaigrette
1 tablespoon Dijon
    mustard
1 tablespoon raw honey,
    melted
juice of 1 lemon
olive oil, to taste
    (optional)

Preheat the grill to 180°C/gas mark 4.

Arrange the figs on a baking tray, cut-side up.

Whisk together the truffle oil, honey and basil in a small bowl and pour this dressing over the figs, reserving a little for later.

Place the figs under the grill and cook for 3–5 minutes, until the sauce starts to bubble up and the figs caramelise.

Pour off the cooking juices into the bowl with the reserved truffle dressing and whisk in the ingredients for the vinaigrette.

Serve the figs on a bed of rocket leaves, dressed with the honey-mustard vinaigrette.

 TIP FIGS CONTAIN MORE FIBRE THAN ALMOST ANY OTHER FRUIT OR VEGETABLE. THIS IS A REAL BENEFIT WHEN YOU'RE ON A DIET, AS THEIR SLOW-RELEASE ENERGY WILL KEEP YOU FEELING FULL FOR LONGER.

MAIN
MEALS

This is one of my favourite meals, as it immediately conjures up images of sitting in a Parisian café with a crisp green salad and a glass of (non-Paleo) red wine.

CLASSIC STEAK
TARTARE

524 calories | 38.4g fat | 15.1g saturates | 2.1g sugar | 1g salt | 41.7g protein | 0.9g fibre

Serves 4

1 white onion, finely chopped
2 tablespoons finely chopped flat-leaf parsley
2 egg yolks, beaten
800g lean beef mince
a dash of Tabasco sauce
1 tablespoon Dijon mustard
1 tablespoon roughly chopped capers
1 garlic clove, finely chopped
1 tablespoon olive oil
freshly ground black pepper
100g salad leaves

Mix all the ingredients except the salad leaves in a large bowl and season with black pepper.

Cover the bowl and chill in the fridge for 30 minutes.

Arrange the steak mix on individual plates (use a ring if you want consistent shapes). Serve with a crisp green salad.

TIP MAKE SURE THE BEEF YOU BUY IS VERY FRESH AND LEAN. GRASS-FED IS BEST FOR THE PALEO PLAN.

VARIATION USE WHITE TRUFFLE OIL IN PLACE OF THE OLIVE OIL FOR A RICHER FLAVOUR.

This dish is so healthy – tuna is a fish with very little to
no fat content and the lemon is chock-full of vitamin C.

SEARED LEMON TUNA
WITH OLIVE TAPENADE

421 calories | 27.9g fat | 4.9g saturates | 0.6g sugar | 1.6g salt | 41.9g protein | 2.8g fibre

Serves 4

4–6 tablespoons extra
 virgin olive oil
4 x 170g tuna steaks
juice of 3 lemons
a handful of fresh chives,
 finely chopped
a few basil leaves,
 shredded
freshly ground black
 pepper
150g rocket leaves

for the tapenade
1 x 200g jar pitted black
 olives
1 tablespoon capers
1 tablespoon chopped
 tarragon
1 garlic clove, peeled
3–5 anchovy fillets
juice of ½ lemon

Either in a food processor or with a sharp knife, finely chop all
the tapenade ingredients, except the lemon juice, to a coarse paste.
Transfer to a bowl, add the lemon juice and stir to combine.

Heat 1 tablespoon of the olive oil in a griddle pan over a medium-high
heat and sear the tuna steaks for 2 minutes on each side. Add the
lemon juice, then take off the heat, add the remaining olive oil and swirl
the pan to mix.

Serve the tuna on a plate, drizzle over the lemony oil and scatter
the chives on top. Finish with a spoonful of tapenade, a scattering
of shredded basil leaves and a few grinds of black pepper. Serve with
a side of fresh rocket leaves.

 TIP IF YOU OVERCOOK FRESH TUNA THEN IT BECOMES THE SAME
AS TINNED, SO MAKE SURE IT IS NICE AND RARE ON THE INSIDE.

Salmon is considered by many to be one of the healthiest foods you can eat – some say the healthiest. It is rich in heart-healthy omega-3 fatty acids and reduces the risk of numerous cardiovascular problems.

HERBED SALMON
WITH LEMON DRESSING

485 calories | 36.5g fat | 5.8g saturates | 1g sugar | 0.5g salt | 37.8g protein | 1.7g fibre

Serves 4

4 x 175g skinless salmon fillets
a handful of fresh basil
a handful of fresh flat-leaf parsley
a handful of fresh tarragon
a handful of fresh chives
a handful of fresh coriander
1 head of broccoli, broken into florets

for the dressing
6 tablespoons olive oil
1 tablespoon Dijon mustard
3 tablespoons lemon juice

Place the skinless salmon fillets in a large sauté pan and cover with water. Set on the stove, bring the water to the boil, and then immediately remove from the heat. Cover the pan with a lid and let stand for 15 minutes while the salmon gently poaches.

Next, make the dressing. Mix all the dressing ingredients together in a small bowl and set aside.

Heap all your herbs together on a chopping board and chop until fine (a mezzaluna is perfect for this).

Set a steamer or colander over a pan of boiling water and steam the broccoli, covered, for 4–5 minutes.

Take the salmon, one fillet at a time, and roll in the herbs so that it is coated on all sides.

Arrange the salmon on a plate and drizzle over the citrussy dressing. Serve with the steamed broccoli.

 TIP SALMON IS A LEAN PROTEIN THAT IS DIGESTED SLOWLY, SO IT KEEPS YOU FEELING FULL LONG AFTER A MEAL. ENJOY A NICE BIG PORTION.

When I first came up with this recipe I used wasabi peas, but as these are not part of the Paleo plan I had to look around for a substitute. The macadamia nuts were the perfect solution. This is one of the best dishes I have made.

WASABI CRUSTED HALIBUT
ON PAK CHOI

673 Calories | 37.4g fat | 5.6g saturates | 1.4g sugar | 0.7g salt | 82.4g protein | 3.4g fibre

Serves 4

2 tablespoons almond
   flour
2 tablespoons sesame
   seeds
1 tablespoon sesame oil,
   plus extra to drizzle
80g macadamia nuts
2 teaspoons wasabi
   powder or paste
1 egg
4 large pak choi
4 x 350g halibut fillets
1 tablespoon olive oil
1 lime, quartered
freshly ground black
   pepper
a handful of fresh
   coriander, chopped

Place the almond flour, sesame seeds, sesame oil, macadamia nuts, wasabi and egg in a food processor and blend until smooth.

Bring a saucepan of water to the boil and steam the pak choi for 5 minutes. Drain and then plunge the leaves into a bowl of iced water to stop the cooking process and keep them green.

Transfer the wasabi mix to a shallow dish and press the halibut fillets into the mixture so they are thoroughly coated on both sides.

Heat the oil in a heavy, non-stick sauté pan and sear the halibut for 2–3 minutes on each side.

Serve the halibut over the pak choi and drizzle with a little sesame oil. Add a squeeze of lime, a twist of pepper and a scattering of coriander.

 TIP THIS DISH IS ALSO LOVELY WITH OTHER TYPES OF FISH AND I PARTICULARLY RECOMMEND BOTH COD AND TUNA.

Sesame with tuna is one of those classic flavour combinations that just works, and adding a little coconut to the mix sweetens it up very deliciously.

SESAME AND COCONUT
CRUSTED TUNA

567 calories | 29.1g fat | 8g saturates | 1g sugar | 0.5g salt | 67.8g protein | 7g fibre

Serves 4

2 tablespoons coconut flour
3 tablespoons sesame seeds
a handful of fresh coriander
1 garlic clove, peeled
2 eggs
4 x 250–300g tuna steaks
2 tablespoons olive oil

rocket salad (see page 110)

Place the coconut flour, sesame seeds, coriander and garlic in a blender or food processor and blitz to a fine grain. Tip this onto a large plate and spread out in a thin layer. Crack the eggs into a bowl and whisk lightly together.

Dip the tuna steaks in the egg and then in the coconut and sesame seed mixture so they are coated on all sides.

Heat 1 tablespoon of the oil in a large, non-stick frying pan and sear the tuna steaks (two at a time) for 1–2 minutes on each side, until the coating has turned golden brown.

Take out of the pan and set aside while you cook the other tuna steaks in the remaining oil.

Slice the tuna into thin strips and serve with the rocket salad.

It is important to keep the prawn heads on for this recipe, as they deliciously flavour the sauce.

PEEL-AND-EAT
PRAWNS

289 calories | 12.5g fat | 1.8g saturates | 0g sugar | 1.2g salt | 44g protein | 0g fibre

Serves 4

4 tablespoons olive oil
1kg large, unpeeled
  prawns, deveined
3 garlic cloves, crushed
1 teaspoon chilli powder
juice of 1 lemon
a handful of fresh basil
  leaves, thinly sliced

Heat the olive oil in a large saucepan over a medium heat and add the prawns, garlic, chilli powder and lemon juice. Cover and cook for 4–5 minutes.

Add the shredded basil to the saucepan and toss to mix. Remove the prawns from the pan, divide between 4 bowls and serve with the cooking juice for dipping.

 VARIATION IF YOU WOULD LIKE TO SPICE UP THE SAUCE EVEN MORE, ADD A FINELY CHOPPED BIRD'S EYE CHILLI.

 TIP THIS IS A CHEF'S TRICK FOR SLICING BASIL LEAVES INCREDIBLY THINLY – ROLL EACH LEAF UP LIKE A CIGAR AND THEN SLICE THINLY. VOILA!

This dish has everything we love about deep-fried food – just without the guilt. Make an extra-large batch, as you'll be amazed how quickly it all goes.

COCONUT PRAWNS
WITH BROCCOLI

406 calories | 31.1g fat | 7.4g saturates | 3g sugar | 0.5g salt | 22.1g protein | 8.4g fibre

Serves 4

400g broccoli florets
2 tablespoons almond oil
   or olive oil
2 tablespoons almond
   flakes
300g peeled King prawns
3 tablespoons coconut
   flour
freshly ground black
   pepper
4 tablespoons olive oil
1 lemon or lime, cut into
   wedges
a handful of coriander,
   chopped

for the dipping sauce
6–8 tablespoons light
   coconut milk
1 tablespoon sesame oil
1 tablespoon sesame
   seeds

Bring a saucepan of water to a simmer over a medium heat and cook the broccoli for 3–4 minutes. Drain and plunge into a bowl of iced water to prevent the florets from cooking any more in their own steam.

Transfer the broccoli to a mixing bowl and toss it in the almond oil and almond flakes.

Put the prawns and coconut flour into a ziplock bag, season with black pepper and shake to coat thoroughly.

To make the dipping sauce, combine all the ingredients in a small saucepan and stir over a low heat. Bring to a simmer and pour into a serving dish.

In a large, non-stick sauté pan, heat the olive oil over a low heat. Add the prawns and cook for about 2 minutes on each side, taking care that they don't burn.

Arrange the prawns and broccoli on a plate, squeeze over the lemon or lime juice and scatter with some coriander. Serve the dipping sauce separately on the side.

 TIP LIGHTLY BATTER THE PRAWNS, AS YOU ONLY NEED A DUSTING OF THE FLOUR TO GET THE BEST OUT OF THIS DISH.

This Italian-inspired dish is all I want to eat when I'm dining al fresco – perfect for a summer lunch in the garden or a dinner under the stars. The salsa verde is fantastic with any fish or seafood and also works well with chicken.

MIXED GRILL
WITH SALSA VERDE

667 calories | 43g fat | 7.3g saturates | 3g sugar | 1.5g salt | 66.4g protein | 4.5g fibre

Serves 4

2 x 200g swordfish
  steaks, cut in half
2 x 200g salmon steaks,
  cut in half
2 x 200g tuna steaks,
  cut in half
2 tablespoons olive oil
freshly ground black
  pepper
1 lemon, cut into wedges

for the salsa verde
1 tablespoon capers
6 tablespoons olive oil
6–8 fresh basil leaves
1 teaspoon Dijon
  mustard
juice of 1 lemon
1 tablespoon chopped
  tarragon
3 tablespoons finely
  chopped shallots

Preheat a griddle pan and brush the fish with 1 tablespoon of the olive oil. Sear the fish in the hot pan for 2–3 minutes on each side. Set aside.

Meanwhile, place all the salsa verde ingredients, except the shallots, in a food processor and blitz until they are finely chopped – you want to keep a little texture, so be careful not to purée them. Transfer to a bowl and stir in the shallots.

Serve the fish with the salsa verde on the side. Finish with a few grinds of black pepper and a squeeze of fresh lemon. This is delicious with a tomato and red onion salad.

I love this dish hot and spicy, so add more chilli if you like. Make sure you don't go over on these cooking times as the squid should be succulent and tender, not rubbery and chewy.

STUFFED SQUID
WITH TOMATO SAUCE

412 calories | 16.4g fat | 3.1g saturates | 4.5g sugar | 1.6g salt | 58.3g protein | 1.4g fibre

Serves 4

8 small squid
300g cooked skinless
  salmon fillet
200g cooked, peeled
  prawns
2 garlic cloves, peeled
2 tablespoons sun-dried
  tomato paste
1 egg
a handful of fresh basil,
  chopped, plus extra
  to garnish
freshly ground black
  pepper
1 tablespoon olive oil

for the tomato sauce
1 tablespoon olive oil
½ red onion, finely
  chopped
1 x 400g tin of chopped
  tomatoes
1 garlic clove, crushed
1 small bird's eye chilli,
  finely chopped
50ml vegetable stock

First prepare the squid. Remove the tentacles and reserve. Pull away the wings, remove the head, and empty the main tube of cartilage and slime. Pull or cut away the eyes and beak, and remove anything else that feels hard or slimy from the tentacles. Discard everything but the cleaned tentacles and main body tube. Wash well and dry.

To make the stuffing, place the salmon, prawns, peeled whole garlic cloves, sun-dried tomato paste, egg and basil in a food processor and purée until smooth.

Fill each squid about two-thirds full with the stuffing and press it down. Secure the end with a cocktail stick and set aside until ready to cook.

To make the tomato sauce, heat the oil in a wide, sauté pan over a medium heat and fry the onion until soft. Add the tomatoes, crushed garlic, chilli and stock and heat to a low simmer, stirring to combine.

Take a non-stick griddle pan and place over a moderate heat. Season the squid with black pepper. Add 1 tablespoon oil to the pan and add the squid. Cook for 2 minutes on one side, then turn over and cook for a further 2 minutes.

Transfer the squid to the pan with the tomato sauce and cook, covered, over a medium to low heat for about 12–15 minutes. Turn half way through the cooking time. Serve the squid with the tomato sauce and some basil scattered on top.

Honey and ginger are two of my favourite ingredients as they create magic when cooked together. Both are also excellent for the immune system so this makes a lovely dinner all through the winter months.

HONEY-GLAZED SALMON
WITH GINGER

707 calories | 44.2g fat | 7.4g saturates | 13.8g sugar | 0.6g salt | 63.8g protein | 4.6g fibre

Serves 4

4 x 300g skinless salmon
  fillets

for the glaze
2 tablespoons raw honey
1 tablespoon Dijon
  mustard
juice of 1 lemon
1 x 2.5cm piece of fresh
  ginger, peeled
  and grated

for the cabbage
3 tablespoons olive oil
1 small cabbage, sliced
  into thin strips
1 garlic clove, crushed
1 tablespoon sesame
  seeds, plus extra
  to garnish
freshly ground black
  pepper
4 spring onions, chopped

Heat a large, non-stick pan over a high heat and add the salmon – if you have a good-quality, non-stick pan, there should be enough oils in the salmon to cook it without the need to add any extra oil. Cook the salmon for 3–4 minutes on each side.

Meanwhile, make the glaze. Place the honey, mustard, lemon and ginger together in a bowl and stir to combine. Set aside.

When your salmon is just about cooked, spoon the glaze over the top, then take off the heat. The glaze will caramelise in the hot pan and turn the salmon sticky and brown.

To cook the cabbage, heat half the olive oil in a wok over a medium heat. Add the cabbage and stir fry for 3–4 minutes, then add the remaining oil and cook for another 5 minutes, tossing all the time (if you need more moisture, add a drop or two of water). Add the garlic and sesame seeds and cook for a further minute.

Turn the cabbage out onto a plate, season with black pepper and top with the glazed salmon. Scatter the spring onion over the top and serve with a few extra sesame seeds.

Macadamia nuts are grown in tropical countries and are one of the more expensive nuts to purchase. However, they are full of health benefits and taste deliciously crunchy and buttery. I highly recommend them.

SALMON WITH MACADAMIA
AND ALMOND CRUST

686 calories | 54g fat | 7g saturates | 2g sugar | 0.3g salt | 45g protein | 3g fibre

Serves 4

75g unsalted almonds
50g macadamia nuts
2 eggs
75g almond flour
2 tablespoons olive or
   almond oil
4 x 175g skinless salmon
   fillets
75g watercress
½ lemon, cut into wedges
freshly ground black
   pepper

Preheat the oven to 200°C/gas mark 6.

Place the nuts in a food processor and give them a quick whizz. Add the eggs, almond flour and 1 tablespoon of the oil and blend.

Place the salmon on a baking tray and spread the nut mix over the top in a thick layer. Bake in the oven for 15–18 minutes.

Toss the watercress in the rest of the oil and a squeeze of lemon and divide between 4 plates. Serve the salmon on top and season with a grind of black pepper.

Nothing beats a good Thai chicken curry and this recipe keeps it nice and authentic. The only thing missing is a bowl of steamed jasmine rice, but when you have flavours this bold and a sauce this creamy, it's no hardship to do without any accompaniment and double-up on curry instead.

THAI CHICKEN
CURRY

439 calories | 19.6g fat | 10.6g saturates | 4.6g sugar | 0.9g salt | 58.9g protein | 4g fibre

Serves 4

2 tablespoons olive oil
1 red onion, sliced
900g skinless chicken
   breast, sliced
1 tablespoon Thai red
   curry paste
400ml light coconut milk
3–4 dried lime leaves
500g spinach
a handful of fresh
   coriander, chopped

Heat the olive oil in a large, non-stick pan and sweat the onion for 3–5 minutes, turning constantly.

Add the chicken to the pan and cook, stirring, for 5 minutes.

Add the curry paste and cook, stirring, for a minute, then add the coconut milk and reduce the heat to low. Add the lime leaves and spinach and simmer, covered, for 8 minutes.

Divide the curry between 4 bowls and serve scattered with fresh coriander.

 TIP ALWAYS MAKE SURE YOU OPT FOR SKINLESS CHICKEN BREASTS WHEN YOU ARE WATCHING YOUR WEIGHT AS THEY CONTAIN ONLY 1G SATURATED FAT PER 100G SERVING.

Chinese food is always a favourite but it's hard to make on the Paleo diet as you can't have traditional soy, oyster or hoi sin sauce. There are alternatives you can try, but here the ginger and coriander provide so much flavour that you really don't need anything else – except maybe a drizzle of sesame oil, if you like.

CHINESE WOK-FRIED CHICKEN WITH GINGER AND HONEY

390 calories | 16.4g fat | 3g saturates | 11.6g sugar | 0.6g salt | 47.1g protein | 5.3g fibre

Serves 4

2 ¼ tablespoons olive oil
1 x 2.5cm piece of fresh ginger, peeled and grated
2 garlic cloves, finely sliced
680g skinless chicken breast, cut into strips
freshly ground black pepper
4–6 baby pak choi, halved
1 tablespoon raw honey, melted
2 red peppers, deseeded and sliced
4 tablespoons chopped coriander, plus extra to garnish
2 tablespoons lime juice (or lemon juice)
60g cashew nuts, chopped, plus extra to garnish
5 spring onions, chopped, plus extra to garnish

In a large, non-stick wok, heat 1 tablespoon of the oil over a medium heat and fry the ginger and garlic until lightly golden. Tip out of the pan.

In the same wok, heat 1 tablespoon of the olive oil over a medium heat. Season the chicken with black pepper and stir fry for a few minutes on each side until brown.

Return the ginger and garlic to the pan, add the remaining olive oil and cook the pak choi for about 4–5 minutes. Add all the remaining ingredients to the pan, tossing everything together and stir frying for 3–4 minutes until the stir fry is a little golden from the honey.

Serve in a bowl with a scattering of spring onion, extra cashew nuts and a few coriander leaves to garnish.

 TIP WHEN STIR FRYING, DON'T BE TEMPTED TO REACH FOR THE MANGE TOUTS OR SUGARSNAP PEAS AS THESE ARE LEGUMES, SO NOT PALEO-FRIENDLY FOODS. LEGUMES CONTAIN PHYTIC ACID, WHICH CAN OBSTRUCT THE ABSORPTION OF NUTRIENTS AND LEAD TO DIGESTIVE PROBLEMS.

This is a lovely BBQ recipe for a hot summer's day and also for when you want to bring the outdoors indoors, as you can cook it in the oven. The sauce is fantastic and I always make double so I can freeze a batch for another time (just make sure you discard any that has come into contact with raw chicken).

PERFECT BBQ
CHICKEN

250 calories | 2.7g fat | 0.7g saturates | 6.9g sugar | 0.7g salt | 49.4g protein | 1g fibre

Serves 4

4 x 200g skinless chicken breasts
150g mixed salad leaves or grilled artichokes (see page 70)

for the BBQ sauce

1 tablespoon raw honey
3 tablespoons tomato paste
1 tablespoon sun-dried tomato paste
2 garlic cloves, crushed
2 tablespoons white vinegar
1 tablespoon dried rosemary
1 tablespoon Dijon mustard

Fire up the barbecue or preheat the oven to 200°C/gas mark 6.

First make the BBQ sauce. Melt the honey in a saucepan over a low heat. Add all the remaining BBQ sauce ingredients, stir well and take off the heat. Divide the sauce between 2 bowls.

Place the chicken in one of the bowls, cover with clingfilm and set aside in the fridge to marinate. Cover with clingfilm and place in the fridge while the barbecue heats up. Cover the remaining bowl of sauce with clingfilm and set aside.

Grill the chicken on the barbecue for 5 minutes on each side or until cooked through. Turn regularly and, each time, brush the chicken with the marinade. (If using an oven, cook for 20 minutes, turning half way through and brushing with the marinade.)

Serve the chicken with a simple salad or grilled artichokes – and don't forget the second bowl of BBQ sauce for extra dipping.

 TIP REMOVING THE CHICKEN SKIN LOWERS THE FAT.

Sadly, school dinners have put a lot of people off calves' liver and it's such a shame as, when it's not overcooked and still a little pink on the inside, it's delicious – especially with a rasher of bacon and a dollop of English mustard on the side.

CALVES' LIVER
WITH ROASTED LEMONS

361 calories | 22.1g fat | 3.5g saturates | 26.3g sugar | 0.2g salt | 14.7g protein | 1.4g fibre

Serves 4

3 tablespoons olive oil
2 medium red onions, finely sliced
2 tablespoons raw honey, melted
freshly ground black pepper
300g calves' liver, thinly sliced
150g mixed salad leaves or rocket

for the lemons
12 unwaxed lemons, quartered
4–6 tablespoons olive oil
4 garlic cloves, crushed
4 tablespoons raw honey, melted

Preheat the oven to 220°C/gas mark 7.

First prepare the lemons. Place the quarters in a roasting tin and mix with the olive oil, garlic and honey. Cook in the oven for 30–40 minutes, or until the lemons have turned golden brown.

Heat 2 tablespoons of the olive oil in a large sauté pan and fry the onions for 3–5 minutes. Add the honey, turn the heat down and cook for a further 3 minutes on a low heat or until the onions are caramelised. Set aside.

Heat the rest of the olive oil in a large frying pan over a high heat. Season the liver and sear for 1–2 minutes on each side (I like mine nice and pink in the middle so would cook for just 1 minute). Serve with the onion and roasted lemons and a mixed leaf salad on the side.

 TIP ALTHOUGH CALVES' LIVER IS MODERATELY HIGH IN FAT, IT IS ALSO HIGH IN ZINC, IRON AND VITAMINS B12 AND B6.

This Greek classic is my go-to recipe for Friday night dinner. It's simple to make but tastes so satisfying that you never get bored with it, plus any leftovers make a lovely Saturday lunch, served cold with a crisp green salad.

GREEK-STYLE
LEMON CHICKEN

517 calories | 15g fat | 3g saturates | 4.7g sugar | 0.6g salt | 90.9g protein | 0.6g fibre

Serves 4

3 tablespoons olive oil
1 tablespoon raw honey, melted
juice of 1 lemon
1 teaspoon cayenne pepper
freshly ground black pepper
1 chicken (approx 2.25kg), cut into 10 pieces
1 whole head of garlic, separated into unpeeled cloves
2 unwaxed lemons, cut into wedges
2 sprigs of rosemary

a handful of flat-leaf parsley, chopped
200g mixed salad leaves or the Greek salad on page 149

Preheat the oven to 200°C/gas mark 6.

In a large bowl, mix the olive oil, honey, lemon juice and cayenne pepper together. Season the chicken pieces with black pepper, add to the bowl and massage the marinade into the skin with your hands.

Place the chicken pieces in a roasting tray and add the garlic cloves, lemon wedges and rosemary. Mix well together and ensure everything is well spread out. Season.

Roast in the hot oven for 40 minutes until the chicken has turned golden brown and the lemons have started to caramelise.

Serve this straight from the roasting tin, with a scattering of fresh parsley and a salad on the side.

 TIP LEMONS ARE ACIDIC, BUT IN FACT THEIR EFFECT ON THE BODY IS ALKALISING AND SO THEY HELP RESTORE BALANCE TO THE BODY'S PH.

Saffron is a very expensive spice, but a pinch goes a long way and it lends a beautiful colour to this roasted chicken.

ROASTED CHICKEN
WITH SAFFRON

444 calories | 9g fat | 2g saturates | 0g sugar | 1.3g salt | 90.6g protein | 0g fibre

Serves 4

1 whole chicken
    (approx. 2.25kg)
1 lemon, cut into 6
    wedges
1 whole head of garlic,
    broken up
1 stock cube, broken into
    4 pieces
1 tablespoon olive oil
1 teaspoon saffron
    threads
freshly ground black
    pepper

Preheat the oven to 220°C/gas mark 7.

Stuff the cavity of the chicken with the lemon wedges, garlic cloves and pieces of stock cube.

Place the chicken in a roasting pan and drizzle over the olive oil. Sprinkle over the saffron threads, season with black pepper and massage the flavourings into the skin.

Roast in the oven for approximately 2 hours or until the juices run clear and the bird is cooked through.

Remove from the oven and serve with a drizzle of the cooking juices and a side of your choice.

 TIP TRY AND BUY FREE-RANGE CHICKENS FROM A TRUSTED, LOCAL SOURCE AS IT'S IMPORTANT TO KNOW THEY FED ON PESTICIDE-FREE GRASS.

If you have good-quality meat and great seasonings, you can often do away with the burger bun and not miss it at all. However, as a Paleo alternative, fry two large portobello mushrooms in a little oil and sandwich the burger between these. You can even sprinkle sesame seeds on top if you like.

BEEF

BURGERS

595 calories | 38.6g fat | 11.8g saturates | 3.9g sugar | 0.7g salt | 57.3g protein | 3.8g fibre

Serves 4

900g lean beef mince
1 red onion, halved
   (1 half finely chopped)
2 tablespoons sun-dried
   tomato paste
2 eggs, beaten
2 garlic cloves, crushed
4 tablespoons almond
   flour
2 tablespoons olive oil
200g mixed salad leaves

Place the mince, chopped onion, sun-dried tomato paste, eggs, garlic and almond flour in a large mixing bowl and stir to combine. Using your hands, shape into 4 equal-sized patties.

Heat the olive oil in a large, non-stick pan over a high heat and cook the burgers for 3–4 minutes on each side. Reduce the heat and cook for a few more minutes on each side until the meat is cooked medium to well-done.

Slice the remaining onion into 5mm-thick round slices. Top each burger with slices of onion and serve over a crunchy green salad.

 TIP AS A GENERAL RULE, THE LEANER THE BEEF, THE BETTER THE BURGER.

This dish is home comfort food at its best. If you want to mix a Green and Red recipe then this one is brilliant with the acorn spaghetti on page 158. The sauce is rich so make sure you buy the leanest mince you can, or mince the meat yourself in a food processor.

ITALIAN

MEATBALLS

546 calories | 31.9g fat | 10.4g saturates | 10.8g sugar | 0.9g salt | 53.9g protein | 4g fibre

Serves 4

850g lean beef mince
½ medium onion, finely
  chopped
2 garlic cloves, crushed
2 tablespoons almond
  flour
1 egg, lightly beaten
1 tablespoon chopped
  flat-leaf parsley,
  plus extra to garnish
4 tablespoons tomato
  paste
1 tablespoon olive oil
torn basil, to garnish

for the tomato sauce
1 tablespoon olive oil
1 garlic clove, crushed
2 x 400g tins of chopped
  tomatoes
4 tablespoons sun-dried
  tomato paste
140ml vegetable stock

First make the meatballs. In a large mixing bowl, mix the mince, onion, garlic, almond flour and egg, using your hands to thoroughly combine. Add the parsley and half the tomato paste and, again, mix well. Using your hands again, roll the mixture into 20 or so balls and set aside.

Now for the tomato sauce. Heat the olive oil in a large casserole dish or saucepan over a medium heat. Once hot, add the garlic and cook gently for a few minutes until aromatic, then add the chopped tomatoes and sun-dried tomato paste and stir to combine.

Heat the remaining tablespoon oil in a large casserole dish over a high heat and cook the meatballs for about 1 minute on each side, turning with a wooden spoon until they are brown all over. Add the tomato sauce, stock and remaining tomato paste. Reduce the heat and cook for 10 minutes, covered, then remove the lid and simmer for another 5 minutes to reduce the liquid.

Serve with a scattering of parsley and basil.

The sesame seeds and sesame oil lend this recipe a slightly oriental feel but then the pine nuts and basil are a little more Italian-inspired. It's a lovely combination – you'll see!

SESAME STEAKS
ON BROCCOLI PURÉE

761 calories | 45.6g fat | 10.7g saturates | 3.3g sugar | 0.6g salt | 83.1g protein | 8.7g fibre

Serves 4

4 tablespoons sesame seeds
4 x 300g sirloin steaks, trimmed of fat
freshly ground black pepper
800g broccoli florets
4 tablespoons chopped garlic
2 tablespoons toasted pine nuts, plus extra to garnish
6–8 fresh basil leaves, torn, plus extra to garnish
6 tablespoons olive oil, plus extra for frying
freshly ground black pepper

Place a single layer of sesame seeds on a large plate and, one at a time, press the steaks down on the seeds to coat them on each side.

Place the broccoli and garlic in a large saucepan of water and cook for 8–10 minutes. Drain, then place in a food processor with the pine nuts, basil, olive oil and black pepper and blend to a textured purée.

Heat a drizzle of olive oil in a large, non-stick pan over a medium heat. Sear the steaks for a few minutes on each side. Remove from the heat. If you like your steak rare, take the meat out of the pan straight away. If you prefer your meat a little more done, leave it to rest in the hot pan for a further 5 minutes before serving.

Serve the steaks over a layer of broccoli purée and garnish with a few toasted pine nuts and fresh basil leaves.

 TIP GOOD STEAK REALLY NEEDS TO BE COOKED RARE. DON'T BE AFRAID OF THIS – THE HEAT KILLS ANY BACTERIA, SO JUST USE THE FRESHEST MEAT YOU CAN BUY AND YOU ARE SET TO GO.

There is another way to cook this: sear the lamb on a hot BBQ for about 3 minutes on each side, then close the barbecue hood, turn off the heat and leave for about 3 hours. I did this by mistake many years ago when I ran out of coal, and it resulted in the best lamb I have ever tasted. It is how the Greeks cook the lamb dish Kleftiko – slow cooking it so it falls off the bone.

ROAST LEG
OF LAMB

509 calories | 21.9g fat | 10.9g saturates | 1.9g sugar | 0.7g salt | 59.7g protein | 1.5g fibre

Serves 6

2kg leg of lamb on the bone
4 garlic cloves, thinly sliced
6 sprigs of rosemary, each cut into 3, plus extra for the gravy
2 tablespoons olive oil
freshly ground black pepper

for the Greek salad
1 cucumber, chopped into chunks
10 cherry tomatoes, halved
24 pitted Kalamata olives, halved
a handful of salad leaves
a handful of mint leaves
1 tablespoon olive oil
juice of ¼ lemon

Preheat the oven to 200°C/gas mark 6.

Place the lamb in a roasting tray and, with a sharp knife, make deep 1cm cuts in the meat in about 15–20 places. Fill each incision with a slice of garlic and a sprig of rosemary. Drizzle over the olive oil and massage into the meat.

Cover the lamb with foil and place in the oven. After 30 minutes, remove the foil, then return the meat to the oven and cook for another hour.

When ready, lift the meat from the roasting tray and rest on a plate for 10 minutes before serving. To keep the lamb warm, you can cover it with the foil you used before.

To make the salad, place the cucumber, tomatoes, olives and salad leaves in a bowl and toss to combine. Scatter the mint leaves over the top and dress with the oil and lemon.

To make the gravy, place the roasting tray on the stove and heat up the cooking juices with 4–6 tablespoons water. Add some chopped rosemary and a twist of black pepper and simmer gently until reduced to a light, flavoursome gravy.

Serve the lamb with the gravy and the fresh Greek salad on the side.

Venison is a meat that is very, very lean, so it's perfect for when you are trying to cut down on fat. If you like your beef cooked rare, prepare venison in the same way – it will be wonderfully tender.

VENISON
ON KALE

632 calories | 34.1g fat | 5.2g saturates | 3.8g sugar | 0.7g salt | 77.1g protein | 6.8g fibre

Serves 4

4 x 300g venison steaks
freshly ground black
   pepper
3 tablespoons almond oil
   or olive oil
½ white onion, chopped
600g kale
1 teaspoon chopped
   capers
juice of ½ lemon
60g almonds,
   roughly chopped
60g toasted pine nuts
1 tablespoon finely
   chopped flat-leaf
   parsley

Season the steaks with black pepper. Heat 1 tablespoon of the almond or olive oil in a large, non-stick frying pan and sear the venison steaks over a high heat for 3–4 minutes on each side. If you like your meat rare, lift the steaks out of the hot pan straight away and transfer them to a plate. If you prefer your meat a little more done, leave the meat to rest in the hot pan for a further 5 minutes.

Meanwhile, heat the remaining oil in a large, non-stick frying pan and fry the onion over a high heat for 3 minutes. Add the kale and cook for 3–4 minutes, then add the capers, lemon juice and nuts. Heat for just a minute, tossing to combine.

Serve the venison over the kale with a sprinkling of parsley to garnish.

 TIP KALE IS ONE OF THE MOST NUTRITIOUS VEGETABLES YOU CAN EAT – ONE SERVING CONTAINS MORE VITAMIN C THAN AN ORANGE AND MORE VITAMIN A THAN ANY OTHER LEAFY GREEN.

This dish contains all the best Italian flavours, although obviously the pesto contains no Parmesan cheese! Parmesan is one of the most high-fat cheeses there is and, by eliminating it, you make the pesto guilt-free. There are so many flavours here that you won't miss it one bit.

ROASTED VEGETABLES WITH PESTO

644 calories | 49.4g fat | 6g saturates | 27.3g sugar | 0.15g salt | 14g protein | 18g fibre

Serves 4

1 butternut squash, peeled and quartered
400g cauliflower florets
600g carrots, peeled and sliced
400g Brussels sprouts
1 red onion, peeled and quartered
4 tablespoons olive oil
freshly ground black pepper

for the pesto
12–16 fresh basil leaves
100ml olive oil
2 garlic cloves, peeled
100g toasted pine nuts

Preheat the oven 220°C/gas mark 7.

Place all the vegetables in a roasting tray and toss with the olive oil and season with black pepper. Cook in the oven for about 40 minutes, tossing thoroughly at the half-way point.

Meanwhile, blend all the pesto ingredients in a food processor and set aside.

Remove the vegetables from the oven, dress with the pesto and serve.

 TIP IF YOU LIKE YOUR SPROUTS A LITTLE CRUNCHY, ADD THEM WHEN YOU TOSS THE VEGETABLES HALFWAY THROUGH.

Cauliflower is delicious in curry dishes and makes a great vegetarian option. You can always spice this up with a little more fiery chilli if you like.

CAULIFLOWER AND MUSHROOM CURRY

326 calories | 27g fat | 16.5g saturates | 5.9g sugar | trace salt | 9.9g protein | 5.2g fibre

Serves 4

1 head of cauliflower, broken into florets
3 tablespoons olive oil
freshly ground black pepper
1 large onion, chopped
3 garlic cloves, crushed
250g button mushrooms
1 x 2.5cm piece of fresh ginger, grated
1 tablespoon ground coriander
1 tablespoon ground cumin
1 tablespoon garam masala
1 tablespoon chilli powder (or more, to taste)
400ml light coconut milk
a handful of fresh coriander, chopped

Preheat the oven to 220°C/gas mark 7.

In a roasting tin, toss the cauliflower florets in 2 tablespoons of the olive oil and season with pepper. Roast for 25 minutes, tossing occasionally until the cauliflower starts to brown. Remove from the oven and set aside.

In a wide, shallow pan, fry the onion in the remaining tablespoon olive oil over a high heat for 3–4 minutes. Add the garlic, mushrooms and ginger and cook for another minute, stirring.

Stir in the spices and cook for a minute, then add the coconut milk. Season to taste. Bring to a boil, then stir in the cauliflower. Reduce the heat, cover the pan, and cook for about 5 minutes on a low heat. Serve with plenty of fresh coriander.

 TIP IF YOU'D LIKE TO MAKE THIS DISH FAT-FREE, SIMPLY REPLACE THE COCONUT MILK WITH VEGETABLE STOCK.

This is perfect for when you have vegetarian friends over for dinner.
It's pretty simple to make but looks impressive, as if you've been
in the kitchen preparing it for hours!

AUBERGINE STACKS
WITH HERB OIL

412 calories | 40.4g fat | 4.8g saturates | 7.2g sugar | 0.1g salt | 5.1g protein | 5.5g fibre

Serves 4

6 tablespoons olive oil
2 large aubergines, sliced
    into 2.5cm-thick
    rounds
2 tablespoons sun-dried
    tomato paste
2 garlic cloves, crushed
80g pine nuts
20–25 cherry tomatoes,
    halved
a handful of fresh basil,
    roughly chopped
freshly ground black
    pepper

for the herb oil
50ml olive oil
handful of fresh herbs
1 garlic clove, finely
    chopped

Heat 2 tablespoons of the olive oil in a heavy, non-stick pan and fry the aubergine slices over a medium heat for about 4 minutes on each side.

Meanwhile, place the sun-dried tomato paste, garlic, pine nuts and cherry tomatoes in a mixing bowl and pour over the remaining olive oil. Toss everything together and add the basil.

Now layer up the aubergine like a tower. Lay the largest slice down as the base and spread a spoonful of the tomato mixture over the top, then add another aubergine slice and continue to layer up until you have a stack about 4–5 slices high.

Blend all the herb oil ingredients together in a bowl.

Serve the aubergine towers with a drizzle of herb oil around the edge of the plate and a twist or two of black pepper.

If you miss potatoes, this is the answer. To me, butternut squash is the best vegetable you can have on the Paleo diet – roast it, mash it, make soups with it and stir fry it, and you'll never have a carb craving again.

BUTTERNUT RATATOUILLE

194 calories | 11.7g fat | 1.7g saturates | 12.7g sugar | 0.1g salt | 3.4g protein | 6.7g fibre

Serves 4

1 small butternut squash, peeled, halved and chopped into small chunks
4 tablespoons olive oil
freshly ground black pepper
1 onion, finely chopped
1 aubergine, chopped into cubes
1 tablespoon tomato paste
2 garlic cloves, crushed
2 large tomatoes, deseeded and diced
a handful of fresh basil, shredded

Preheat the oven to 220°C/gas mark 7.

Place the butternut squash in a roasting tray and toss in 2 tablespoons of the olive oil. Season with black pepper and cook for 25 minutes, tossing halfway through.

Meanwhile, heat 1 tablespoon of the olive oil in a large sauté pan and sweat the onions for 2 minutes, then add the aubergine and cook, tossing for 5 minutes.

Add the remaining olive oil, tomato paste, garlic, tomatoes and roasted squash. Stir all the ingredients to mix thoroughly and cook for a further 4–5 minutes.

Serve hot or warm with a garnish of fresh basil and an extra twist of black pepper.

 TIP AUBERGINES ARE FULL OF DIETARY FIBRE, SO WILL KEEP YOU FEELING FULL AND STOP YOU BEING TEMPTED TO SNACK.

For me, this is the best dish in the book. Whenever I feel a carb craving coming on, this is the recipe I reach for. I have not stopped making it since the first attempt and I hope you will try it and love it too.

SPAGHETTI ACORN SQUASH

279 calories | 12.3g fat | 1.8g saturates | 22.2g sugar | 0.2g salt | 8g protein | 11g fibre

Serves 2

2 tablespoons olive oil
1 acorn squash, halved and peeled into long ribbons
2 courgettes, peeled into long ribbons
2 garlic cloves, crushed
175g cherry tomatoes, halved
2 tablespoons sun-dried tomato paste
freshly ground black pepper
a handful of fresh basil leaves

Heat 1 tablespoon of the olive oil in a large, non-stick pan and add the squash. Toss over a medium heat for 3 minutes, then add the courgette and cook for a further 2–3 minutes.

Add the remaining olive oil, plus the garlic, tomatoes and tomato paste and cook for 2–3 minutes, stirring to coat. Reduce the heat to low and toss.

Remove the pan from the heat and turn the contents onto a plate. Season with black pepper, tear over the fresh basil and serve.

 TIP YOU REALLY WON'T MISS CARB-HEAVY PASTA ONE BIT WHEN YOU'VE TRIED THESE LOVELY RIBBONS OF SQUASH – THEY HOLD A SAUCE FANTASTICALLY WELL SO TRY THEM WITH ALL SORTS OF TOPPINGS.

DESSERTS

Some desserts leave you feeling guilty and bloated, but this one does neither. It has a wonderful Mediterranean feel about it and makes you want to dine al fresco and savour every bite.

GRILLED FRUIT WITH CINNAMON AND HONEY

193 calories | 3.2g fat | 2.5g saturates | 38.4g sugar | 0g salt | 3.7g protein | 6.6g fibre

Serves 4

4 nectarines, halved and stoned
6 figs, halved
4 plums, halved and stoned
2 apples, quartered and cored
1 cinnamon stick, broken
2 tablespoons raw honey
1 tablespoon coconut oil
2 teaspoons ground cinnamon

Preheat the grill to a moderate heat.

Place all the fruit on a roasting tray and mix together. Tuck the pieces of cinnamon stick into any gaps.

In a small saucepan, heat the honey and coconut oil together. Drizzle this syrup over the fruit, then place the roasting tray under the grill and cook for 3–4 minutes until the fruits caramelise and darken.

Serve in bowls with a sprinkling of ground cinnamon.

 TIP USE WHATEVER FRUITS ARE IN SEASON FOR THIS DISH – PLUMS, APPLES, BLACKBERRIES, RASPBERRIES, PINEAPPLE, ETC. – ALL ARE DELICIOUS!

This pudding will take you back to your childhood,
I guarantee you. It's the perfect thing to whip up at a moment's notice.

BANANA PUDDING

235 calories | 10.2g fat | 9.1g saturates | 30.6g sugar | 0g salt | 2.4g protein | 1.8g fibre

Serves 4

4 ripe bananas
400ml light coconut milk
1 tablespoon raw honey
fresh mint, to garnish

Place the banana, coconut milk and honey in a blender and blitz until smooth.

Divide the mix between 4 ramekin dishes and chill in the fridge for 30 minutes.

Serve with a sprig of fresh mint.

This is a great dessert that always reminds me of Thailand. It
tastes very indulgent, but in fact there's nothing to feel guilty about at all.

CARAMEL BANANAS

276 calories | 9.9g fat | 1.9g saturates | 41.7g sugar | 0.3g salt | 3.9g protein | 3g fibre

Serves 4

4 ripe bananas, peeled
1 tablespoon coconut oil
400ml light coconut milk
3 tablespoons raw honey
3 tablespoons sesame
  seeds

With a sharp knife, thickly slice the bananas on an angle.

Heat the oil in a heavy, non-stick sauté pan over a high heat and cook the bananas for about 2 minutes.

Add the coconut milk and honey, reduce the heat and simmer for 5 minutes.

Spoon the bananas into small bowls and serve with a sprinkling of sesame seeds.

As a child, I loved going to Chinese restaurants, as their sesame, apple and banana desserts were always my favourite. This dish is a far healthier option and yet it still reminds me a little of those fantastic childhood flavours.

FRIED CINNAMON BANANAS

274 calories | 14g fat | 12g saturates | 33.7g sugar | 0g salt | 2g protein | 3.3g fibre

Serves 4

4 ripe bananas, peeled
3 tablespoons coconut oil
2 tablespoons raw honey
1 teaspoon ground cinnamon
4 tablespoons coconut flakes

Using a sharp knife, quarter each banana lengthways (so you have 4 long strips).

Heat the oil in a frying pan over a low heat and cook the banana slices for 2–3 minutes.

Lift the bananas out of the pan and drain on kitchen paper. Discard the oil from the pan.

Return the bananas to the pan and place over a medium heat. Add the honey and cinnamon and toss to coat, cooking for about a minute until golden. Add the coconut flakes and serve.

 TIP NUMEROUS STUDIES HAVE SHOWN THAT CINNAMON IS VERY EFFECTIVE AT REGULATING BLOOD SUGAR. IT ALSO ADDS A DELICIOUS FLAVOUR TO ALMOST ANY COOKED FRUIT, SO ADD A DUSTING TO PLUMS, BANANAS, PINEAPPLE, APPLES... YOU NAME IT.

This is the best way to have ice cream on the Paleo diet.
However, be aware that, as you are not using cream, the coconut milk
can crystalise in the freezer to make a more granita-type ice. For a creamier,
more mousse-like texture, try freezing for just 30 minutes.

COCONUT AND ALMOND
ICE CREAM

319 calories | 25.7g fat | 11.9g saturates | 14g sugar | 0g salt | 6.4g protein | 0.5g fibre

Serves 4

100g almonds
480ml light coconut milk
3 tablespoons raw honey

Place the almonds in a ziplock bag and bash them with a rolling pin until they resemble rough crumbs.

Mix the almond crumbs in a bowl with the coconut milk. In a saucepan, warm the honey over a low heat, and then drizzle into the bowl, stirring to combine.

Pour the mixture into a freezer-proof container and freeze for at least 2 hours before serving.

COCONUT AND MANGO
ICE CREAM

243 calories | 19g fat | 17.1g saturates | 14.9g sugar | 0g salt | 2g protein | 3.2g fibre

Serves 4

1 mango, peeled and
   chopped
2 tablespoons raw honey
480ml light coconut milk
80g coconut flakes
fresh mint leaves,
   to serve

Place the mango in a blender with the honey and blitz until smooth.

In a bowl, combine the coconut milk with the coconut flakes. Pour in the mango purée, reserving a little for later, and stir to combine.

Pour the mixture into a freezer-proof container and freeze for at least 2 hours.

Serve in a martini glass, drizzled with the reserved mango purée, and garnished with a fresh mint leaf.

Pineapple is full of natural sugar, so when you combine it with honey and heat, you get a wonderful, sticky, caramelised result.

GRILLED
PINEAPPLE

115 calories | 0.3g fat | 0g saturates | 28.6g sugar | 0g salt | 0.8g protein | 2.8g fibre

Serves 4

juice of 1 lemon
1 pineapple, peeled
   and cut into wedges
   or slices
3 tablespoons raw honey
a dusting of ground
   cinnamon
a few mint leaves, finely
   chopped

Squeeze the lemon over the pineapple pieces so they don't discolour. Drizzle over the honey and toss so it is thoroughly coated.

Heat a griddle pan over a medium heat and, when hot, add the pineapple and griddle for 4–5 minutes on each side until it caramelises.

Dust the pineapple with ground cinnamon to serve and scatter over the chopped mint to garnish.

 TIP SWEET AND DELICIOUS, PINEAPPLE IS PACKED FULL OF NUTRIENTS – FULL OF ANTIOXIDANT PROTECTION AND IMMUNE SUPPORT.

I don't believe that diets should take out all the enjoyment from life, and so this recipe means you can still enjoy cake and not break any Paleo rules. It's perfect with a cup of morning or afternoon herbal tea.

LEMON
POUND CAKE

412 calories | 33.1g fat | 13.7g saturates | 9.7g sugar | 0.2g salt | 13.5g protein | 6.9g fibre

Serves 6

6 tablespoons coconut oil,
    plus extra for greasing
4 tablespoons raw honey
185g almond flour
60g coconut flour
4 eggs
zest and juice of 1 lemon
    (or 1 tablespoon
    lemon extract)

Preheat the oven to 180°C/gas mark 4 and lightly oil a round 23cm cake tin.

Place a small saucepan over a low heat and melt the coconut oil and honey. (You can also do this in the microwave for about 30 seconds.)

In a large mixing bowl, combine the almond and coconut flour. Add the melted honey and oil mixture, eggs, lemon zest and juice and whisk together to mix well.

Pour the cake mix into the prepared tin and bake for 30 minutes or until a thin skewer inserted into the centre of the cake comes out clean.

Remove the cake from the oven and leave in the tin until completely cold. Turn out onto a plate and serve with a cup of herbal tea.

 TIP ALMOND FLOUR AND COCONUT FLOUR IS EASY TO BAKE WITH - IT'S JUST A LITTLE DRIER THAN REGULAR FLOUR, SO YOU NEED A LITTLE MORE EGG TO BIND EVERYTHING TOGETHER.

Carrot cake made its debut in the 1960s, although carrot has been used as a sweetener since medieval times. In any case, it is very appropriate to use it in this way to make this wonderfully tasty Paleo cake.

CARROT

CAKE

559 calories | 38.1g fat | 17.4g saturates | 31.3g sugar | 0.4g salt | 16.8g protein | 11.2g

Serves 6

6 tablespoons melted
   coconut oil, plus extra
   for greasing
4 tablespoons maple
   syrup
165g almond flour
60g coconut flour
1 teaspoon freshly
   ground nutmeg
1 teaspoon ground
   cinnamon
400ml prune juice
6 eggs, beaten
1 teaspoon vanilla
   extract
4 large carrots, peeled
   and finely grated
40g shredded dry coconut
60g raisins

Preheat the oven to 190°C/gas mark 5 and lightly oil a 21 x 11cm loaf tin.

Place a small saucepan over a low heat and melt the coconut oil and maple syrup. (You can also do this in the microwave for about 30 seconds.)

In a large mixing bowl or food processor, combine all the remaining ingredients and mix together well.

Pour the cake mix into the prepared tin and bake for 30 minutes or until a thin skewer inserted into the centre of the cake comes out clean.

Remove the cake from the oven and leave in the tin until completely cold. Turn out onto a plate and serve with a cup of herbal tea.

This is a tried-and-tested traditional dessert that has been tweaked only slightly to substitute the sugar for raw honey, so it's all good on the Paleo diet. The lime zest is a lovely addition and lifts the palette at the end of the meal.

POACHED
PEARS

138 calories | 0.2g fat | 0g saturates | 35.3g sugar | 0g salt | 0.7g protein | 5.g fibre

Serves 4

juice and zest of 2 limes
8 small pears, peeled,
  with stems still on
750ml water
4 tablespoons raw honey
a few drops of vanilla
  essence

Pour the lime juice over the pears to stop them from turning brown.

Transfer the pears and lime juice to a large saucepan. Sit the pears upright in a large pan and cover with the water and honey. Bring the water to the boil and simmer for about 10 minutes, or until the pears are tender all the way through when pierced with a skewer – cooking times will vary depending on the ripeness of your fruit.

Remove the pears with a slotted spoon and arrange on a serving plate.

Add the vanilla essence to the poaching liquid and boil to reduce by half, stirring occasionally. Set aside to cool.

Serve each pear with the cooled syrup and a garnish of lime zest.

 TIP PEARS ARE FULL OF FIBRE (24% OF YOUR RDA) SO KEEP YOUR DIGESTIVE SYSTEM IN SHIP-SHAPE CONDITION.

INDEX

ACKNOWLEDGEMENTS

I am extremely grateful to my nephew, Alexander Green, a recent graduate from Oxford who, with his valuable research, has made a huge contribution to this book.

It has been such a pleasure to work with Kyle Books again. Kyle has always seen that my passion in creating healthy food that is full of flavour. After losing 29kg (4½ stone) myself many years ago, I know what a struggle it can be, and so I love to hear feedback from readers about their weight-loss progress. Please follow me on Facebook: Chef Daniel Green